THE CENTURY OF SCIENCE

WATSON DAVIS

EDITOR

SCIENCE TODAY

NEW WORLD OF SCIENCE SERIES

THE ADVANCE OF SCIENCE

ATOMIC BOMBING

SCIENCE NEWS LETTER

AUTHOR

THE STORY OF COPPER

SCIENCE PICTURE PARADE

FROM NOW ON

THE CENTURY OF SCIENCE

THE
CENTURY
OF
SCIENCE

BY WATSON DAVIS

DUELL, SLOAN AND PEARCE
NEW YORK

First edition

Affiliate of
MEREDITH PRESS
Des Moines & New York

Library of Congress Catalogue Card Number: 63-16824

MANUFACTURED IN THE UNITED STATES OF AMERICA FOR MEREDITH PRESS

VAN REES PRESS • NEW YORK

CONTENTS

THE CENTURY OF SCIENCE

PROLOGUE

IN ITS EFFECTS upon civilization, the twentieth century so far shows more power and swiftness of pace than did any such span of the past. Great as were the times of Darwin and Pasteur, the epochs of Newton, Galileo, and Copernicus, and even the almost infinitely long periods of the evolution of fire and wheel, today seems the most intellectually explosive era of mankind.

Two great wars wrenched peoples, minds, and material things on the face of the earth. Wars are certainly no novelty to mankind, and the First and Second World Wars of the twentieth century did not set the tone of our times.

Our tempo and distinction come from the discoveries and applications of science and technology. This is the scientific century.

There have been revolutions in the span of about two generations, revolutions that are more sweeping than the overthrow of any tyrant or the toppling of any system of economics, philosophy, or religion.

Man no longer envies the birds. For spanning oceans, plains, and mountains, there are airplanes that can fly as fast as the sweep of sunrise and sunset. The automobile has spread our own neighborhood farther than a horse can go in a day. Rockets protect us. They will transport us, even into outer space.

Chemists make superior textiles so cheap that silkworms are virtually out of jobs. Cotton is dethroned.

3

In every living room television shows history being made. Everyone has his own private theater. Imploring voices, great music, and blatant entertainment are to be had at the flick of a radio switch.

To keep warm in winter, almost no one shovels coal any more. Something can be done about the summer's heat. Light from filaments and glowing gases blazes day and night to confound the curse of darkness and increase time for work and play.

Infectious diseases have met their wonder drugs, and we live longer and die of degenerative disorders, such as those of the heart and cancer. All this, not much longer than a century after Pasteur. Vitamins and other food factors have made eating a benefit to health as well as a source of energy and a pleasure. Freezing has joined the tin can in preserving food. Radiation from exploding atoms is providing another technique of preservation for lean years and remote places of the plentiful harvests that scientific agriculture provides.

The new agriculture, with mechanization, improved plants, the control of insect plagues and plant diseases by chemicals, allows us to hope that the productivity of the soil can keep pace with human fertility. The dire prophecy of Malthus has not been fulfilled, but the world is in the midst of a population explosion the like of which has never before occurred. Food may even keep ahead of hunger.

Machines that "think" routinely (at least as well as uninterested and unimaginative humans) have begun to take over some of the burdensome and menial tasks of our complex industries and daily life. They can keep accounts, control and guide manufacturing, run elevators, pilot airplanes and rockets, route our telephonic communications, and perform with unhuman accuracy thousands of other operations.

Freud gave us insight into our unconscious, explaining why we behave the way we do. Einstein has built a new universe for us and along with it a new philosophy. Astronomical discoveries of a vast far-flung cosmos, seemingly exploding, give us glorious perspective and humility. We are upon a bit of matter, whirling about a rather less than ordinary star, one of billions of stars in one of billions of "universes." Ah, ego?

We know over a hundred chemical elements. Man made some of them and will make more. We know some stable subatomic particles, building blocks of what we call matter—electron, proton, neutron—and a host of other fleeting ones. Molecules we make by the thousands upon thousands, some of great industrial importance, such as those for drugs, dyes, and plastics.

We have discovered where the earth has hidden its stores of liquid energy—petroleum. Intoxicated with such unearned power, we spend it profligately, unmindful of the leaner days to come when oil shale and coal will be more troublesome to use. We still have the sunshine unused.

We have split the atom—and some wish that atoms had not fissioned and had not been fused. For matter is energy, as Einstein said when the century was young, years before the first controlled nuclear reaction in a former squash court at Chicago and the first atomic explosion at Alamagordo. The atomic age is upon us, binding our minds in secrecy, poising an H-bomb over the heedless heads of all men, and irradiating the human future. It promises unlimited power, especially when the thermonuclear reaction of the H-bomb is tamed and harnessed.

Some things the gay nineties saw we still use, although few ideas or objects have escaped at least face-lifting.

The methods of our progress arose in the centuries past. Galileo, Newton, Pasteur, and the other great inventors discovered revolutionary facts. But they did more. They developed and proved the methods and techniques of discovery in the modern world, the so-called experimental method that topples false authoritarianism no matter how firmly entrenched. This is the great human invention. It is the essence of progress.

So magnificently has this fundamental method been applied that the results have been bountiful and spectacular.

This century will be remembered, not primarily for world wars, but, as Toynbee suggests, as "having been the first age since the dawn of civilization, some five or six thousand years back, in which people dared to think it practicable to make the benefits of civilization available to the whole human race."

Our scientific age builds upon the past and supports the onrushing future that is ever upon us.

CHANGING
ATOMS

THE ATOMS were once thought to be immutable. Until about the turn of the century, there was nothing so stable and unchanging as the atoms, conceived to be the smallest particles of matter. Forerunners of things to come were the discoveries of Roentgen and Becquerel that atoms in motion and in transformation produced radiations that could be detected by means of photographic plates, much in the manner of light, but these radiations are much more intense and penetrating than light.

The X-rays of Roentgen had their first application in medicine, allowing bones and foreign objects within the body to be made visible, a great aid to surgery. The first doctors and physicists who made use of this new phenomenon of radiation from a metal target bombarded by electrical discharges paid for their enthusiasm with harmful damage to their hands and sometimes fatal injuries from exposure to the X-ray radiation. Years later there were other martyrs to the imperfect knowledge of the dangers of radiation emitted by various devices, devices that culminated in nuclear explosions.

The time-honored stability of the physical world was shaken again by Becquerel's discovery of radioactivity, the disintegration of uranium and concomitant production of radiation. Then came the classic discoveries of the Curies and the isolation of radium and associated elements, with utilization of the phenomenon of radioactivity.

Pierre Curie

Marie Curie

This ushered in the era of changing atoms, an era not ended and still rushing onward.

The little particles of matter, once visualized as atoms, proved to be complex in their composition, and because of this very complexity they could be transmuted into other forms of matter.

The great dream of the Middle Ages was to change base metals into gold. The alchemists searched vainly for the philosophers' stone. Changing atoms did not fulfill materialistically the hopes of such selfish transmutation. Instead of producing gold the research in physics gave us knowledge and accomplishment more to be desired than precious metal.

Radioactivity, naturally occurring and uncontrollable by human effort, is true transmutation, the conversion of one element into another. Later as the atomic age progressed, it became possible to achieve elemental changes to order. Some of these built up atoms, and others tore them asunder.

Reaching a culmination in atomic bombs, this revolution in physics in the twentieth century has, in effect, transmuted the world into a new kind of social organism in which every area, no matter how remote, can be affected potentially by any other area that possesses atomic weapons, the means of delivery, and maniacal ill-will.

Artificial transmutation in the elements, which has become so important in our utilization of matter and energy, began when Rutherford in 1919 literally knocked H out of nitrogen. The H in this case stands for hydrogen, the lightest of the elements. This is what happened in this first artificial transmutation of matter. The atom of nitrogen weighing 14 on the usual scale of atomic weights was bombarded by a swift charged particle of helium weighing 4, which was shot out from a radioactive substance. The helium particle momentarily coalesced with the nitrogen atom, becoming a mass of atomic weight 18. Then this combination split into two entirely different substances, the hydrogen nucleus or a proton weighing 1 and an unusual type of oxygen atom that weighs 17. Only about one out of a million of Rutherford's alpha-particle projectiles scored hydrogen-producing hits.

The oxygen variety of mass 17 formed in this bombardment was a quite new kind of substance, for this oxygen isotope was un-demonstrated in 1919. It was not to be identified until more than a decade later.

While economic history may count the year 1919 as worth re-

**Sir Ernest Rutherford,
Lord of Nelson**

membering because of the signing of the Treaty of Versailles, which formalized the ending of the World War, that year is much more likely to live in the memory of the generations to come as the year in which Rutherford smashed the atom.

The hydrogen that Rutherford knocked out of nitrogen by bombarding it with alpha particles from radioactive disintegrations gave fresh life to a century-old hypothesis. It is that hydrogen, lightest of the chemical elements, is the stuff out of which all of them are made. Rutherford's experiment gave belated fame to Dr. William Prout, early nineteenth-century Edinburgh physician, whose contention that hydrogen was a fundamental building block of the elements was considered the height of fancy by his contemporaries.

Rutherford's pioneering seems feeble in comparison with the violent smashing of atoms practiced in decades since, but the methods he used are typical of the ways of atomic experimentation.

The new physics with its profound effects upon social structure and human beliefs was not born of brilliant experiments alone. Fruitful theory was written by the mathematical pencils of the physicists who used scintillations of their brain cells rather than radioactivity of atoms. Repeatedly theory has guided experiment and then explained the meaning of the experimental results inspired by the testing of these theories.

Einstein was the outstanding theoretical architect of the atomic era. His 1905 formulations both remade the universe of space and time and set forth the relationships of matter and energy that led to the nuclear bombs and atomic power.

E equals mc^2 is the most powerful equation in the modern world. E is energy, m is mass, and c is a constant, the velocity of light. The transformation of mass into energy that this Einstein equation predicted was, when enunciated, seemingly fantastic and something that could not really affect the practical world. It was the stuff of science fiction. Certainly no sane businessman would invest money because of it. Some far-seeing scientists were bold enough to translate its possibilities into predictions that an ocean liner might be propelled across the Atlantic with power contained in the mass of a teaspoonful of water—a prediction that literally is not yet fulfilled, although the use of deuterium extracted from seawater in nuclear fusion power plants of the future may well justify it before the century is ended.

Albert Einstein and formula relating to relativity.

The whole advance of modern physics is based on the idea that things are not what they seem. Common sense gives way to lack of reliance upon the primary human senses. This is particularly true in the exploration of the nearly infinitesimal by the means of mathematical physics. These theories and postulates began with Planck's quantum theory early in the century, which underlay Einstein's fruitful atomic formulations. There followed the theoretical delvings into atomic structure of Bohr, Sommerfeld, Heisenberg, Born, Jordan, de Broglie, Dirac, Schroedinger, and others, producing conceptions of the atom and its structure that must be pictured primarily in equations. These theoretical advances built the solid formation of the atomic age, for they suggested the revolutionary experiments.

Not until the Second World War and the dramatic release of atomic energy did the atomic advances of the new physics have a major impact upon the world at large. In the interval between the two great World Wars, when mankind was not yet aware of the imminence of the second global upheaval of war, probing into the heart of matter and its constitution progressed quietly in laboratories all over the world. The resources for such research were meager in comparison with the major research of World War II and afterward. In no science has there been more international co-operation than in physics, at least in the days between the two World Wars. This may have been because the practical results of physics were not evident, and neither industry nor the military was greatly concerned about possible monopolies of knowledge and their consequences in this field.

The advances in physics occurred in a considerable number of areas.

There was great curiosity as to the constitution of matter and the make-up of atoms. In addition to Prout's fortunate surmise as to the fundamental nature of hydrogen as a building block of the elements, in 1897 J. J. Thomson discovered the electron, with negative electrical charge equal and opposite to the positive of the proton, which is the heart or the nucleus of the hydrogen atom. For some time it was thought that these two particles made up the whole of the universe. But in 1932 as a result of atomic bombardment it was discovered that there exists a neutral particle known as the neutron, with a mass equal to that of the hydrogen atom, that is, the proton, about 1,800 times heavier than the electron.

These three particles, electron, proton, and neutron, are the standard interchangeable parts of atoms. The protons and neutrons make up the nucleus of the atoms except that in the case of hydrogen its heart or nucleus is simply a proton alone. The structure of the atom may be thought of as a solar system although physicists do not encourage such visualizations. The nucleus corresponds to the sun at the center. The electrons are planets.

In the early days of the century, particularly in research in England, it was found that the alpha rays from radioactive substances are high-speed helium nuclei and that there are atoms of different atomic weight having exactly the same chemical properties. These were called isotopes. Isotopes were to play a major role in the whole development of the atomic era, for when the crucial discovery of the fission of uranium was made in 1939, making possible the release of nuclear energy, it was found that the U-235 isotope of uranium was fissionable whereas the other isotopes naturally present in the element were not. Almost every element consists of twins, triplets, or quadruplets, quintuplets, sextuplets, and even more. Most striking perhaps is double-weight hydrogen known as deuterium, which was discovered in 1931–32 by an American team. Later it was found that hydrogen is actually triplets with a third, triple-weight hydrogen isotope, tritium, which presumably plays an important role in the hydrogen, or thermonuclear, bomb.

Experimentation was prodded by theory and accelerated through the thirties. The positive electron or positron was first revealed by cosmic rays smashing into matter. It was then artificially created by bombardment of matter with the gamma rays from radium. The positron is a positive counterpart of the electron.

Between the masses of the negatively and positively charged particles, electrons and protons, there are mesons, "strange particles" intermediate in mass, and positive, negative, or neutral. They are observed in destruction caused by cosmic rays, and in the giant atom smashers they are being used for atomic research. Their role seems to be that of a sort of "glue" holding particles together in the atomic nucleus.

In this almost infinitesimal world of the atom, there is a dichotomy of particles and radiation that is not easily resolved. In one view radiation may be considered particles and in another particles seem to be radiations. For example, the gamma rays given off by radium and X-rays are electromagnetic radiation similar to X-rays and light. But even these act very much like particles because of their short wave lengths. It is possible to think of a "particle" or quantum of gamma radiation as very much the same thing. Such a particle or quantum of radiation is called a photon.

Radiation is emitted from radioactive atoms as short-length gamma rays, and all atoms when excited by high temperatures or by electric discharge may emit light rays. These, spread out by refraction, make up the bright lines of spectra characteristic of the chemical elements. Most of our information about the structure of atoms is derived from these spectra.

Some of the knowledge about atomic constitution is obtained

Professor E. O. Lawrence holding the first cyclotron shown to the National Academy of Sciences, Berkeley, Calif., in 1930.

by observing the extremely powerful, somewhat mysterious cosmic rays, which seem to be born in the reaches of outer space. These radiations plunged into the atmosphere of the earth, fragmenting the atoms of the atmosphere and smashing them with a great display of atomic fragments. Physicists have had no machines that could emit radiation approaching the billions of electron volts of energy of the cosmic rays, although there have been built in the United States and Russia giant accelerators that have achieved the energies of at least the lower ranges of the cosmic rays.

One of the unsolved mysteries of the universe is the origin of cosmic rays. This is undoubtedly bound up in the unsolved puzzles of the constitution of the universe itself.

One of the great inventions in the acceleration of atomic particles was Dr. E. O. Lawrence's cyclotron, now a widely utilized device for atomic research with several hundred of them in operation.

Cyclotrons under Lawrence's direction at the University of California in Berkeley, did much of the pioneer creation of new elements beyond No. 92 in the atomic table, uranium.

Plutonium was created in a cyclotron. Plutonium achieved unusual importance because of the fact that it was fissionable and hence capable of being used in atomic bombs.

Before the developments that led to the release of atomic energy there were believed to be only ninety-two chemical elements, some of them undiscovered. In atomic energy development transuranium elements were created by bombardment of

Original cyclotron, University of California, sixty-inch, two-hundred-ton. Professor E. O. Lawrence is at the right.

lesser elements. So far eleven have been artificially created in this way with the heavier ones extremely radioactive and short-lived.

No chapter in human history is more important and significant than the discovery and understanding of these atomic events, which occurred largely during that part of the twentieth century prior to World War II. Two axioms of physics state: (1) Matter can be neither created nor destroyed; (2) Energy can be neither created nor destroyed. For all practical purposes these axioms were true and separate principles until about 1940. Now it is known that they are, in fact, two phases of a single principle, for it was discovered that energy may sometimes be converted into matter and matter into energy. The laws of conservation of matter and of energy must be combined and, when there is transformation of matter into energy, there results the destruction

The beam of deuterons from this sixty-inch cyclotron of the Argonne National Laboratory shines with ultraviolet light as its particles strike the molecules of the air.

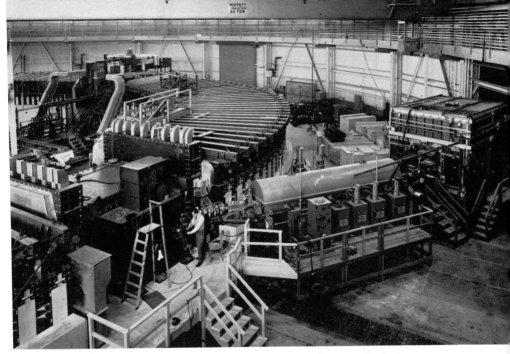

6.2 BEV University of California Bevatron Proton Synchrotron, Berkeley, Calif.

12.5 BEV Argonne Zero Gradient Proton Synchrotron (high-energy research center still under construction at right) at Argonne National Laboratory, Argonne, Ill.

Aerial view of Alternating Gradient Synchrotron, Brookhaven National Laboratory, Upton, Long Island, N.Y.

Inside the tunnel of the Brookhaven Alternating Gradient Synchrotron.

of matter and the creation of energy. This has been demonstrated with awe-inspiring results in the atomic bombs—the fission bombs made with uranium and plutonium—and to an even greater extent in the thermonuclear, or fusion, bombs that use light elements as their fuel.

This conversion of matter into energy is important to us in another way because it is presumably the mechanism that keeps the stars stoked with a constant outpouring radiation. Since the sun is a star and since we are dependent upon the sun for our light, heat, and very existence, this is a phase of atomic energy that compensates in some measure for the dangers of destruction that constantly confront the world in an atomic era.

Perhaps in some of the other stars and other locations in the universe, the opposite transformation, that of the destruction of energy in the creation of matter, is in process of building up the substance of the universe around us so that all will not eventually become heat and light.

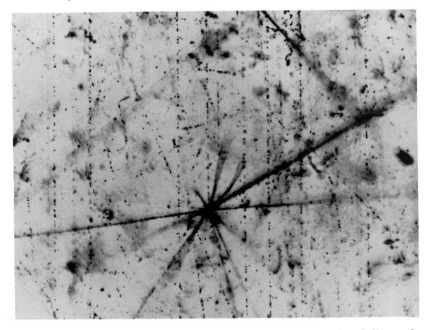

Strange nuclear reactions—A photographic emulsion exposed to billion-volt protons from the cosmotron at Brookhaven National Laboratory, Upton, Long Island, N.Y., shows the strange nuclear reactions from which physicists are learning about the nucleus. A high-energy proton, disintegrating an atom in the emulsion from which ten particles flew out, caused the "star."

THE
ATOMIC
REVOLUTION

THE TAPPING of the energy of the atom has had more far-reaching consequences than the invention of gunpowder. The atomic energy breakthrough achieved in only a half dozen years during World War II is perhaps the greatest historical event in human history. Into the hands of the political and military leaders was thrust almost unimaginable military power of destruction and subjugation. For peaceful uses—the supply of power for industry and everyday living—atomic energy is almost inexhaustible, giving mankind the opportunity to continue its profligate level of existence. Only the discovery and development of an economical means of utilizing solar energy could have more important consequences in the future energetics of the world.

It is significant for a world, now shrouded in such scientific secrecy, to realize that the fundamental discovery of uranium fission was made in Germany under one of the most cruel and rigorous dictatorships of all times. Because Hitler and his cohorts were not alert to the possibilities of science, the traditions of science's internationalism and free exchange of research proved powerful enough to assure open publication even in wartime of Otto Hahn and F. Strassmann's basic discovery of the fission of uranium, accompanied by the release of more energy through conversion of atomic mass than had been necessary to produce the reaction. This discovery, though part of a long series of discoveries relating to matter and energy, was the breakthrough which

First picture of atomic bomb element—A compound of plutonium, isotope 239, one of the first pure compounds ever isolated, is shown as a colored cloudy mass resting on the rather thick bottom of a test tube. What is seen is about twenty micrograms of greenish-brown plutonium hydroxide and magnification is about fifty diameters.

made it clear that an atomic bomb was possible, that there could be plentiful power for the world from the conversion of matter into energy, and that a new power era had dawned.

The period between this fundamental discovery and realization of the atomic bomb was shorter than that for many other discoveries. Nevertheless, it took about a year for the possibility of an

Gigantic gaseous plant for the enrichment of Uranium 235 to be used in atomic bomb, Oak Ridge, Tenn.

atomic bomb to be realized and acted upon in scientific, government, and military circles. In this interval, research produced a host of new discoveries that laid the groundwork for the coming atomic project, code-named Manhattan.

Never before had such intensive and extensive resources in money, brains, manpower, and international co-operation been

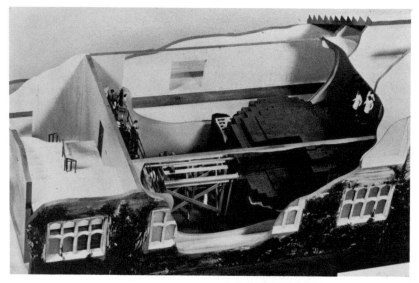

FROM ARGONNE NATIONAL LABORATORY

Model of first atomic pile. One of mankind's most historic steps, the first harnessing of the atom's might, took place in the prosaic surroundings of a squash court, shown here in a realistic artist's conception: Stagg Field, University of Chicago, Dec. 2, 1942.

put into one enterprise. The timetable reads: the fission of uranium with the release of energy became known in 1939, the Manhattan project began in 1940, the first self-sustaining nuclear reaction in an embryonic atomic "pile" was achieved in 1942, and atomic bombs were exploded in test and in war by 1945.

As the dropping of atomic bombs on Hiroshima and Nagasaki proved devastatingly, one such bomb could destroy a city and could release more explosive power than multiple fleets of bombers of the most advanced type carrying conventional explosives.

In 1945, one airplane could carry the explosive power of atomic bombs equivalent to twenty thousand tons of TNT (Nagasaki

Original pile at the west stands of Stagg Field at the University of Chicago —first picture taken, December 2, 1942.

First atomic bomb, "Little Boy," at Hiroshima, Aug. 6, 1945.

load). Astounding as this seemed at the time, it was dwarfed by the destructive power of thermonuclear weapons, or hydrogen bombs, which were to come later.

Except for two bombings of Japanese cities in the closing days of the war, World War II was fought with relatively conventional weapons. The further development of atomic bombs, including those of the thermonuclear sort, gives the world the uneasy assurance that never again will the rival nations be without weapons of almost total destruction should they decide to engage in the insanity of armed conflict. The United States had a monopoly on the atomic bomb when it was first developed, but not many years later Soviet Russia made its own atomic bomb. The great secret about the atomic weapon was how it could be made to explode. Once that was known, the scientists of any other nation with adequate scientific manpower and resources could reach the same goal, as demonstrated by the Soviet achievement. The original atomic bombs derived their energy from the splitting up of heavy elements, uranium isotope 235 and plutonium, into lighter elements with the transformation of some of the mass into energy. More powerful are the thermonuclear weapons developed in the years after World War II and first exploded on Nov. 1, 1952. These so-called hydrogen bombs fused the lighter chemical elements, probably double-weight hydrogen (deuterium) and triple-

First atomic blast, New Mexico, July 16, 1945.

weight hydrogen (tritium), to make heavier elements with a release of energy converted from matter. The thermonuclear weapons are immensely more powerful, being rated in terms of millions of tons (megatons) of TNT.

The thermonuclear bombs are very close to being the ultimate weapons, provided they can be delivered swiftly by intercontinental ballistic missiles to their targets—great concentrations of humanity in an opposing country.

The two kinds of atomic bombs are not independent because, to ignite thermonuclear weapons, a fission bomb must be exploded producing the millions of degrees' heat necessary to bring about the fusion of the lighter elements in the thermonuclear bomb.

From the standpoint of the world's safety and of civilization's survival, the greatest menace for the future lies in the rivalry of two great powers, the U.S.S.R. of the East and the U.S.A. of the West, each capable of dealing totally destructive blows to the other. The fashioning of atomic weapons was an achievement of

Atomic bomb explosion during one of the tests made at the Eniwetok Proving Grounds casting its reflection on the water, spring 1948.

Atomic cloud rising from Bikini Lagoon in Pacific Marshall Islands after explosion of fission bomb in test July 1946.

science. Absence of international means of controlling them is a social and political failure, potentially disastrous to the world.

If the world can stay at peace, atomic energy promises enough power when oil, gas, and coal are exhausted or become too expensive to be utilized. Einstein's famous mass-energy equivalence formula shows that one kilogram (2.2 pounds) of matter, if converted entirely into energy, would give 25 billion kilowatt-hours of energy. Contrast this with the heat produced by burning one kilogram of coal, 8.5 kilowatt-hours of energy. Granted that in fissioning uranium or plutonium in an atomic power plant a complete conversion of matter into energy is not possible; nevertheless, the advantage is so great on the side of the atoms that

Experimental thermonuclear or "hydrogen" detonation. Operation IVY was conducted by Joint Task Force 132, for the Atomic Energy Commission and the Department of Defense, at A.E.C.'s Pacific Proving Grounds in Marshall Islands in the fall of 1952.

the future usefulness and superiority of atomic power plants are assured.

The practical introduction of atomic power has occurred in applications in which the advantages of nuclear energy overrode the normal technological inertia and the economic considerations.

The first major atomic development for electrical energy took place in Great Britain, where the cost of coal-generated power likely will be higher than that of atomic energy. Large installations in the United States were developed more slowly, rather for the purpose of obtaining experience applicable to the future and abroad than because of immediate economic needs.

Most spectacular was the application of atomic power to submarines, freeing them of the necessity of refueling except after long periods of operation and enabling them to voyage submerged as long as human endurance allows. The experience of the *Nautilus* on its long submerged trips, including that under the Arctic ice and the North Pole, showed what achievements were possible and introduced a new kind of shipping to the world.

Atomic power station—The world's first large-scale atomic station, Calder Hall, Cumberland, England, is now pouring some of its energy into Britain's national electricity grid.

Oil-fired vessels will be as obsolete soon as wooden sailing ships became in the nineteenth century. Navies of the future will be atomic in their propulsion as well as their armament, and the telling superiority in any naval conflict will be on the side of the atomic vessels.

The success of the thermonuclear, or hydrogen, bomb immediately aroused hope for a new kind of atomic power using the fusion rather than the fission reaction. The fusion of heavy hydrogen (deuterium), triple-heavy hydrogen (tritium), and perhaps of other light chemical elements such as lithium into heavy elements releases transmuted matter as energy. If this can be done on a large scale, under control and non-explosively, there would be safer and, perhaps, cheaper atomic power. It may take the rest of the century for this achievement.

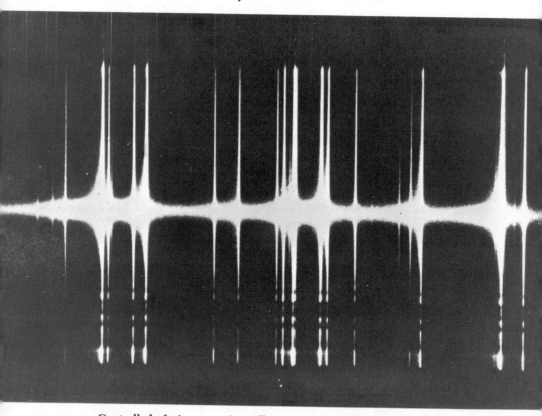

Controlled fusion reaction illustrates research conducted by the Los Alamos Scientific Laboratory of the U.S. Atomic Energy Commission in the field of controlled thermonuclear reactions.

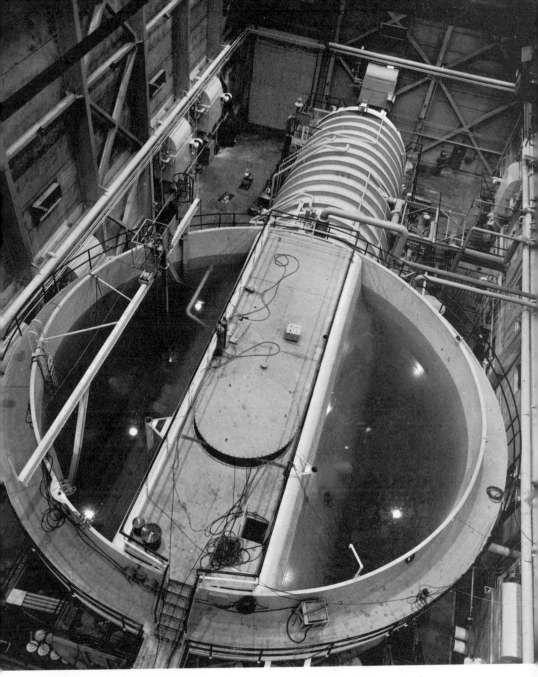

World's first atomic engine—The world's first atomic engine to produce power in substantial quantities—the land-based prototype of the atomic-powered submarine, U.S.S. Nautilus—is housed in this banjo-shaped hull constructed here in the Idaho desert, Arco, Idaho. Both the prototype power plant and the one in the Nautilus, the world's first nuclear-powered submarine, were designed and built by Westinghouse Electric Corporation under contract with the Atomic Energy Commission.

Fuel charge installed in first U.S. full-scale atomic power plant at Shipping-port, Pa. The heart of the nation's first full-scale atomic-electric generating station—this fifty-eight-ton, multi-million-dollar nuclear core, or fuel charge—is shown as it was slowly being lowered into position with its precious fuel consisting of fourteen tons of natural uranium and 165 pounds of highly enriched uranium. Engineers and technicians of Duquesne Light Company and Westinghouse Electric Corporation are seen here supervising the delicate maneuvering of the huge core.

Controlled fusion: the Stellarator. A demonstration model, part of the U.S. Fusion Exhibit at the Geneva Conference, which shows the magnetic field pattern of a "figure-eight"-shaped Stellarator.

Fusion power would represent an almost inexhaustible source of energy for the future, for the oceans contain immense extractable amounts of deuterium. If power production by fission of uranium and uranium-derived atomic fuels would become outmoded, the menace of the by-products of atomic fission power plants would be eliminated. Whenever fission occurs in bombs or in power plants, it produces radioactive material. Most of the dangerous wastes of power plants must be disposed of by burial deep in the earth or in the sea, a procedure that may contaminate the oceans for centuries just as the debris of atomic explosions radioactively dirties the atmosphere.

A fortunate consequence of fission power is the availability of radioactive materials that are useful industrially, medically, and scientifically. These are radioactive isotopes, forms of chemical elements made by the splitting of atoms or by the effects of radiation. Separated from spent atomic fuel or manufactured in atomic reactors, the isotopes' prime utility consists in their artificial radioactivity, which lasts for half-lives of from a few hours to thousands of years, depending upon the isotope. The exploding

The National Bureau of Standards recently acquired a 50,000-curie cobalt 60 source. The cobalt 60 is contained in twelve stainless steel capsules, a sample of which Dr. Scott Smith is shown examining. During transit from Oak Ridge National Laboratory to the Bureau's Washington, D.C., Laboratories, the capsules were placed within a five-ton, water-cooled container. (Note water connections on top of the container.)

atoms give off radiation. If the radioisotope is used as a label to mark the path of a chemical in a life process or an industrial process, its radiation can be detected by special devices. Doctors may use an isotope to place radiation in a particular location of the body for diagnosis or treatment, as in the accumulation of radioactive iodine for patients with thyroid goiter. Cobalt-60 substitutes for radium or X-rays in producing intense radiation that may be used either for cancer treatment or metal inspection. The whole atomic industry might be justified by the value and usefulness of radioisotopes alone.

Radioactivity, little older to science than this century, has become the basis of numerous industries and techniques. Human

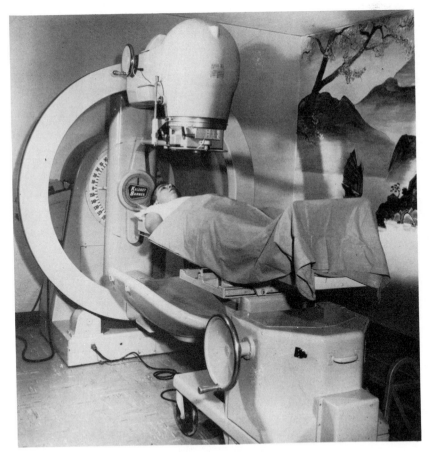

WALTER REED ARMY MEDICAL CENTER

Cobalt 60 Source—Radiation machine with patient.

brainpower and manipulations cannot change the rate or the intensity of radioactivity in nature or of isotopes once they have been created artificially. But new applications of radiation, radio-activity, and atomics will arise in the future just as surely as the radioactivity of existing elements will continue into the months, years, and centuries ahead.

Eight-story cavity created by "GNOME," the first peaceful nuclear detonation at Carlsbad, N.M.—A huge cavity was created 1,200 feet underground in a salt bed twenty-eight miles southeast of Carlsbad by the Gnome detonation on Dec. 10, 1961, in the first experiment in peaceful uses for nuclear explosives, conducted for the U.S. Atomic Energy Commission by the Lawrence Radiation Laboratory, Livermore, Calif.

THE
DISCOVERY
OF THE
UNIVERSE

THE UNIVERSE around us is explored by astronomers who receive light and radio waves that started earthward when the earth itself was young and the evolutionary climb toward man was far in the future.

In this century, the time-scale and extent of the universe have been multiplied repeatedly. Modern astronomy has continued the exploration of the universe which can be considered to have begun in earnest when Copernicus, in the sixteenth century, held that the earth rotates on its axis and that the sun, not the earth, is the center of the solar system.

It is difficult to get a good idea of the immensity of the universe as we now know it. If we rush outward in our imagination away from the earth, traveling at the speed of light, the universe's highest possible speed, we come to the sun eight minutes away. We can ignore the earth's natural satellite, the moon, and the relatively insignificant artificial satellites which man only recently has put into orbit around the earth. Very close to us also, cosmologically speaking, are the planets which are the earth's fellow members of the sun's family.

The nearest star is about four light-years away—actually the double star, Alpha Centauri, with a tiny third component. To have some idea of the vastness and emptiness of space, one must realize that the light-year, the distance that light travels in a year at its rate of 186,000 miles per second, is six trillion miles. The

Harlow
Shapley

whole solar system occupies a sphere that light can traverse in less than half a day.

From the somewhat average sort of star which is our sun, one travels out into the universe and finds a great system of stars called our galaxy. This is the spiral nebula galaxy which we see spread out over the sky as the Milky Way and to which the bright stars belong, some one hundred billion of them. One of the great achievements of astronomy in this century has been the demonstration that the sun is not the center of our Milky Way, as was first thought. Just as Copernicus dethroned the earth from the center of the solar system, so Harlow Shapley proved from studies of the arrangement of globular star clusters in space that the sun lies somewhere between twenty-five thousand and thirty thousand light-years away from the center of a galaxy which is some eighty thousand light-years across.

Another great advance was the discovery that spiral nebulae such as our own Milky Way system exist in great numbers as independent galaxies, or vast aggregations of stars, and that these extend far beyond the limits of our system.

There are probably close to a hundred million galaxies within reach of the world's largest telescope—the two-hundred-inch Hale reflecting telescope on the top of Mount Palomar in California.

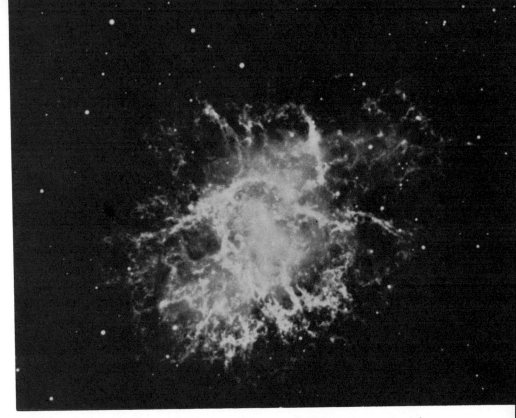

"Crab" Nebula in Taurus—Messier 1, taken in red light, the remains of supernova of A.D. 1054. From a two-hundred-inch photograph.

It whirls in space—This spiral nebula, NGC 628, is in the constellation of Pisces and is photographed by the two-hundred-inch Hale Telescope at Palomar Observatory. The spiral shown here is one of the brighter ones in the sky and is about five million light-years (one light-year equals six million million miles) from the earth. It is moving away from the earth at a speed of approximately three hundred miles per second.

George
Ellery
Hale

It seems likely that the faintest galaxies that have been photographed are at distances on the order of two billion light-years
away from us. This vast expanse of space populated by such a
myriad of galaxies, each with billions of stars, is but a small portion of a still greater unobserved universe.

It is but human to ask whether this great universe of galaxies
is finite or infinite. Our observations do not show any boundary
to the universe in any direction, although the blackness of the
night sky is taken as evidence against an infinite universe.

Albert Einstein's formulation of relativity, one of the two great
contributions that he made to the understanding of nature, throws
light upon the size of the universe through its interpretation of the
red shift or the recessional velocity of distant galaxies. This refers
to the startling observation that the farther away a galaxy is from
us, the greater the shift of its spectral lines toward the red end
of the spectrum, interpreting it as an effect of an expansion in
which everything is rushing away from everything else. Edwin
P. Hubble found this relationship between recession and the
distance of a galaxy, estimating that galaxies 700,000,000 to
800,000,000 light-years away from the sun were rushing away at
the rate of one-fifth the velocity of light.

This so-called red shift has given rise to the idea that we live in an expanding universe. If you figure back according to the rate of expansion, you will find that all of the universe was packed in a very small volume approximately four billion years ago. The Lemaître theory of the universe visualizes a cosmic atom exploding at that time, beginning our universe as we know it. This is but one suggestion of the origin and evolution of the universe. There is also a theory of continuous creation of matter—put forth by British cosmologists, Bondi, Gold, and Hoyle—which conceives of the universe in a steady state. The observed red shift is accounted for in this theory by the continuous creation of hydrogen atoms, so that the universe would not need to have a beginning or an end. Moreover, it would not be necessary to assign fixed dimensions to it. A decision between the two views of the universe is not possible at the present time.

Until the third decade of the twentieth century the universe was of necessity viewed by light alone, captured by great telescopes, recorded by photographic plates as well as the human

The two-hundred-inch dome of Mount Palomar Observatory in California. Both Mount Wilson and Palomar Observatories are largely the result of the lifework of one man: the astronomer, George Ellery Hale.

eye. But in 1931 K. G. Jansky, studying radio transmission, discovered that radio waves come to the earth from distant sources apparently distributed along the Milky Way.

This ushered in a great period of radio astronomy. Astronomers were able to use radio telescopes, great and scrawny, hundreds of feet in diameter, in order to observe the radio emanations from the heavens, day and night, regardless of the weather. Radio waves pass through clouds and fog and, because they are many thousands of times as long as light waves, they do not require the extreme optical accuracy of reflectors. We receive the cosmic radio waves on gigantic receivers that have been built in all parts of the world, away from electrical disturbances. Formerly astronomers who worked with light from the heavens needed darkness and lack of interference from city lights; they now must locate radio telescopes in areas where radio disturbances are minimized.

The Great Nebula of Andromeda made with one-hundred-inch telescope of the Mount Wilson Observatory of the Carnegie Institution of Washington.

Dr. Edwin P. Hubble, astronomer at the Mount Wilson Observatory, whose photographs have revealed for the first time the stars of which the spiral nebulae are made.

The strong sources of light in the sky do not necessarily correspond to those from which radio waves are received. But the radio waves do have a shift toward longer wave-lengths similar to the red shift. Also, a very strong radio source in Cygnus has been identified as a collision between a pair of galaxies approximately 200,000,000 light-years from the sun, and in this case the optical evidence corresponds with radio astronomical evidence for a recession corresponding to that distance.

Individual stars have long been studied and classified by size and kind. The ancients drew their star maps. Telescopic photographs have allowed making maps of fainter and fainter stars, thousands upon thousands of them. Astronomers have been able to classify the stars by their spectra and to work out, in conjunction with magnitude and color, their probable life history from their formation by gravitational contraction of interstellar gas to their white dwarf stage which leads to the stellar graveyard.

Interstellar gas and dust have been studied. This gas is believed to be an almost perfect mixture of hydrogen and helium, with perhaps the hydrogen atoms outnumbering the helium ten-to-one. It is such stuff that stars are made of, probably in the remote depths of space. There is the cosmic dust that shows itself by dark nebulae obscuring the rich starry background that would otherwise be seen.

Whether gas, dust, or blazing stars, all the universe's elemental material seems to be the same as here on earth. In the early part of the century it was thought there was a hypothetical element, nebulium, in the Orion nebula and also other gaseous objects that yielded strange green spectrum lines. But quantum theory allowed physicists to perceive, at least in diagrammatic outline, the electronic structure of the various atoms, indicating that nebulium was double-ionized oxygen. One element, technetium, found in certain stars, did not seem to exist here on earth until it was produced by artificial fission in connection with the atomic bomb, as well as by bombardment of molybdenum in the cyclotron.

The dome of the great hundred-inch telescope at the Mount Wilson Observatory near Pasadena, Calif.

The great hundred-inch telescope at the Mount Wilson Observatory near Pasadena, Calif.

The universe consists almost completely of two gases, hydrogen and helium, which account for all but 2 per cent of all matter. The abundance of heavier elements here on earth makes our earth a rather atypical part of the universe.

The earth has long been known to have variations in its magnetism. The solar corona, seen most effectively during solar eclipse, showed polar rays that suggested electric or magnetic forces emanating from the sun. In 1908 George E. Hale did discover the magnetic field of sun-spots and, since then, magnetism has been recognized in many astronomical phenomena from the magnetic fields of stars themselves to the part that magnetism plays in the sun-spot cycle behavior of variable stars, the origin of

Abbé G. Lemaitre, mathematician, proponent of the expanding universe hypothesis.

1936 PHOTO BY WATSON DAVIS

cosmic rays, the alignment of interstellar dust rings, and even the evolution of stars in spiral galaxies and other cosmic forms.

The sun, so important to earth dwellers as the source of almost all the earth's energy, has had intensive study which has been made simpler through B. Lyot's invention of the coronagraph, a device allowing observation of the sun's corona at times other than the few fleeting moments of total eclipse. Great solar storms and radiation, as well as the light and heat that keep the earth alive, are being charted intensively. This research promises better understanding of many earthly phenomena, including the course of weather in broad outlines.

There have been major advances in collecting the intensity of starlight, even beyond the construction of immense mirrors. More sensitive photographic emulsions have increased the usefulness of existing telescopes manifold. The phototube, a device for accurate measurement of intense light, has even proved superior to photographic plates. Telescopic images are allowed to fall on the sensitive metallic surface which emits electrons in numbers proportional to the intensity of the light received. The electrons are then focused on a photographic plate by a magnetic or electric field, after the manner of an electron microscope. These image-multiplier tubes are creating a new dimension in light astronomy, just as radio and electronic devices are bringing a new era of radio astronomy.

Thanks to earth-circling artificial satellites, it is possible to obtain an unobstructed view, twenty-four hours a day, of the universe and particularly the sun. The visible light reaching the earth's surface does not tell the whole story of the sun's luminous outpourings, nor does it reveal everything about radiation from outer space. Astronomers expect that satellite observations will record much of the radiation from outer space, particularly in the ultraviolet spectrum which is now absorbed by the earth's atmosphere.

The planetary family of the sun now seems to have been completed by the discovery in this century of tiny Pluto, most distant planet from the sun. Pluto was found by a Kansas farm boy, Clyde Tombaugh, who left his home-made telescope to engage in Lowell Observatory's searchings for the transneptunian planet. Its sus-

Radio telescope with 250-foot dish at Jodrell Bank in England, administered by the University of Manchester.

pected influence on other planets had convinced Percival Lowell
that it must exist, and his conviction inspired his associates to
continue to seek it even after his death.

This century's extraordinary development of the knowledge of
the universe has philosophical and practical implications on the
thinking of mankind. Man, so far as we can ascertain, is alone in
the universe. Certainly, in the solar system there is no possible
abode for another kind of humanity. Among our fellow planets,
only Mars offers any possibility of life, and that would be of a
very low order, such as mosses, lichens, or algae. Among the billions of billions of planets, it is possible that there are some that
have conditions resembling those that gave rise to our earth and
the life upon it. But we cannot be sure. We continue to think of
ourselves, for all we know, as being isolated and alone in a vast
universe. We can continue to be confident of man's uniqueness
in the universe, because it does not seem possible for us in the
near future to discover whether we are on the only habitable
planet in the vast universe.

Since we cannot resolve this mystery, we must content our-

**Planet Pluto, outermost of sun's family, shown as a faint object on an
astronomical photograph.**

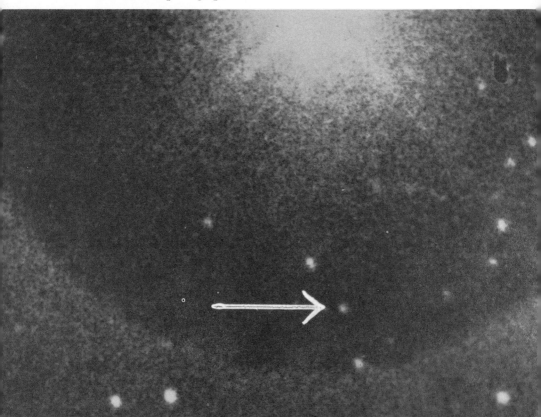

The "Big Dish"—Federal scientists with the Naval Research Laboratory designed a giant radio telescope, with seven-acre reflector, at Sugar Grove, W.Va.

selves with the vast knowledge about the universe that has been accumulated in a relatively small number of years of this century. We can be pleased, as both astronomers and geologists are, by the consistency of the astronomical age determinations of the universe with the cosmic age derived by geologists from the decay of radioactive elements in rocks and meteorites—a matter of from seven to thirteen billion years. We can be confident that this exciting cosmological exploration will continue in the future so long as scientific curiosity, ingenuity, and man's thirst for progress continue.

THE EARTH
AND THE
SCIENCE
THEREOF

HUMANITY lives normally within a thin layer on the surface of the earth, extending a few miles down into the earth and a larger number of miles, but still comparatively few, upward into the atmosphere.

The approximate sphere which is the earth has been barely scratched by human activities. The layers of the earth have been penetrated farthest by oil-seeking drills to a depth of 25,340 feet, almost five miles. The deepest mine is over two miles down where it is much too hot for comfort.

Man's deepest diving took him to 35,800 feet (Jan. 23, 1960) in the U.S. Navy's bathyscaphe, Trieste, an undersea vessel which withstood the immense pressure of the ocean's depths.

The highest mountain rises to 29,028 feet. People live successfully at a height of two miles or more. Yet the flight altitude of scheduled, pressurized jet transports is greater, some 35,000 feet. And military planes can rise even higher, the records being 91,249 feet for jets and 126,000 feet for rocket aircraft. The record altitude of human flight, a man projected by rocket into outer space, will soon be that of the moon, or Mars, or Venus.

Just a few miles below our feet we cannot be sure of the constitution of the earth, although earthquake waves and geophysical experiments give us solid bases for our speculations. Geologists are sure that the fanciful ideas of hell beneath the crust of the

50

earth are not correct, and that volcanoes where they occur are mere blisters on the earth's surface.

The earth may have a heart of gold. It certainly has a solid, heavy metallic heart, a core that is dense and under great pressure, where the heavier metals are segregated and concentrated.

Until the middle of the last century, the past history of the earth was in dispute. The glorious record of the rocks, the story of evolution as told in the layers of the earth, and the fossils of past life through millennia of millennia of time had not been demonstrated.

Geologists and paleontologists have puzzled out the earth's past, from the time that its crust solidified until our own geologic time, the recent epoch when the seas and continents took on their familiar aspect millions of years ago. In some inhabited parts

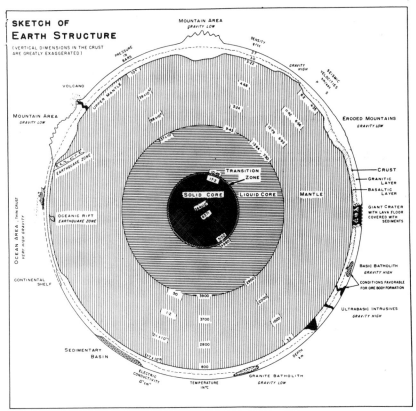

GEOLOGICAL SURVEY OF CANADA

Sketch of earth structure.

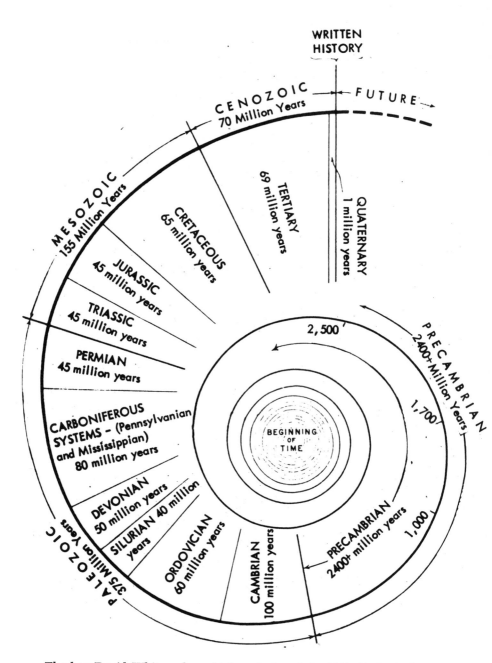

The late David White, when chief geologist of the U.S. Geologic Survey, devised this time chart of geology in spiral form suggested by the whirl of a nebula. Time divisions were brought up to date by Dr. George V. Cohee, Chairman, Geologic Names Committee, U.S. Geological Survey, based on the authoritative time scale of Dr. Arthur Holmes, 1960 revision.

of the globe, mountains have been smoothed off, channels dug and waters diverted, but all that man with his giant earth-moving machines, his massive masonry structures, and even earth-moving by atomic explosions has been able to do is insignificant compared with the changes that geologic time, slow but patient, has wrought.

Measured against the timetable of the earth, man has just arrived upon the rising tide of evolution. Civilization is hardly a thin veneer upon a few spots of the earthly sphere.

True, some of the acts of man have potential effects accelerated far beyond the rate of past change and consequences. When the atmosphere is poisoned with radioactivity, as atomic explosions have begun to do, the conditions necessary for life may be destroyed. The earth will continue to circle the sun, night will follow day with the twirling of the globe, but, if it heaps enough abuse on the comparatively thin troposphere, humanity will not survive to see it. Even the mild radioactivity already added by man's atomic effort to that created by cosmic rays may be sufficient to change the course of human evolution for the worse. Changes in human heredity by mutational modification of the genes could have untold effects on future generations.

What other depredations man did and can perpetrate upon the earth and its surroundings are problematical. There has been some fear that a rise in carbon dioxide in the atmosphere may affect the climate. Carbon dioxide, as the product of combustion of coal, gas, and oil, can hardly duplicate the conditions of the lush vegetational eras when coal was formed, since the concentration of this gas was believed to have been very much higher at that time than it could possibly be from our industrial civilization. More serious are the modifications of environmental conditions resulting from the removal of forests, the pollution of streams and rivers, and the rearrangements of the balance between man and flora and fauna.

It will take a little more time-perspective to assay just what has happened in this century, but the pace of earth modifications seems swifter than in centuries past. After all, the earth is old, very old, perhaps three billion years since its crust cooled and it settled into its planetary orbit. Perhaps the earth is not as old as the rest of the universe, but our century in its time scale is little more than a microsecond of human life.

This twentieth century is notable for the growing realization of the truth of organic evolution which was one of the greatest discoveries of the nineteenth century. The record of the rocks has been more closely delineated. The very landscape testifies to the changing earth; the gradual change that it demonstrates affects man's thoughts and philosophies. The idea of miracles in creation lost its appeal in the light of scientific fact and reason.

With the prodigious use of unrenewable natural resources— coal, oil, gas, iron, lead, tin, copper, and dozens of elements even more scarce—man, the waster, became fearful that he would be forced to mend his profligate ways. The dire threats that there would, in one lifetime, be an end to bountiful petroleum, proved much too pessimistic as great new oil fields were discovered. The use of liquid and gaseous fuel continued merrily—for automobiles and trucks, for diesel trains and ships, for home and industrial heating, and even for electrical power generation. Why not continue to use wastefully the stored sunshine of past eras when the atomic discoveries promised to turn matter into energy—uranium, thorium, and even plentiful deuterium (heavy hydrogen) into nuclear power? Industry turned to plastics made from oil, and to aluminum to supplement iron and steel, not because of a shortage of iron ore but because these newer materials had superior qualities. To the rescue of iron-hungry industry came the finding of great iron deposits which, although more remote, nevertheless kept the blast furnaces roaring.

Repeatedly, there has been apprehension that we shall run out of mineral riches created in the earth during the long evolution of the globe. The use of some of these geological bonanzas is so recent (a mere century in the case of oil) that mankind is hardly accustomed to them or, conversely, so accustomed that it is difficult to imagine being without them. It seems that, whenever in recent decades the shortage scares have been most acute, new reserves have been found, so that the use of oil, iron, and other natural resources could continue merrily. Or better substitutes have been found. Even the great shortages of water in areas of dense population promise to be eliminated by a half-dozen methods of desalting the inexhaustible water of the seas.

During the next few generations the richness of the earth seems capable of maintaining a luxurious civilization for the relatively few of mankind in the industrialized parts of the world.

MAJOR STRATIGRAPHIC AND TIME DIVISIONS IN USE BY THE U. S. GEOLOGICAL SURVEY			
Era	System or Period	Series or Epoch	Estimated ages of time boundaries in millions of years Holmes [1] / Kulp [2]
Cenozoic	Quaternary	Recent	
		Pleistocene	1 —— 1
	Tertiary	Pliocene	11 —— 13
		Miocene	25 —— 25
		Oligocene	40 —— 36
		Eocene	60 —— 58
		Paleocene	
Mesozoic	Cretaceous[3]	Upper (Late)	70 —— 63
		Lower (Early)	
	Jurassic	Upper (Late)	135 —— 135
		Middle (Middle)	
		Lower (Early)	180 —— 181
	Triassic	Upper (Late)	
		Middle (Middle)	
		Lower (Early)	
Paleozoic[3]	Permian[3]	Upper (Late)	225 —— 230
		Lower (Early)	270 —— 280
	Carboniferous Systems — Pennsylvanian[3]	Upper (Late)	
		Middle (Middle)	
		Lower (Early)	
	Carboniferous Systems — Mississippian[3]	Upper (Late)	
		Lower (Early)	350 —— 345
	Devonian	Upper (Late)	
		Middle (Middle)	
		Lower (Early)	400 —— 405
	Silurian[3]	Upper (Late)	
		Middle (Middle)	
		Lower (Early)	440 —— 425
	Ordovician[3]	Upper (Late)	
		Middle (Middle)	
		Lower (Early)	500 —— 500
	Cambrian[3]	Upper (Late)	
		Middle (Middle)	
		Lower (Early)	600 —— 600?
Precambrian[3]		Informal subdivisions such as upper, middle, and lower, or upper and lower, or younger and older may be used locally.	3,000+

[1] / Age values given are the Holmes time scale (Holmes, A., 1960, A revised geological time scale: Edinburgh Geol. Soc., Trans. v. 17, pt. 3, p. 204).
[2] / Ages given are the Kulp time scale (Kulp, J. Laurence, 1961, Geologic time scale: Science, v. 133, no. 3459, p. 1111).
[3] / Includes provincial series accepted for use in U. S. Geological Survey reports.

Terms designating time are in parentheses. Informal time terms early, middle, and late may be used for the eras, and for periods where there is no formal subdivision into Early, Middle, and Late, and for epochs. Informal rock terms lower, middle, and upper may be used where there is no formal subdivision of a system or of a series.

GEOLOGIC NAMES COMMITTEE, 1962

Maintaining the gains that have been made, we can hope that research and development will rescue us from future shortages and also that the expansion of technology to the have-not and know-not areas will let them lift themselves by their bootstraps.

There are practically no undiscovered areas of the earth. Geo-

Adm. Robert E. Peary, who discovered the North Pole, April 6, 1909.

graphically the globe has been conquered. The highest mountain has been scaled. The deepest ocean has been sounded. The ends of the earth have been reached, not just once but many times. Trackless deserts, dense jungles, and remote sea areas have practically all been visited, by air above them if not by the more arduous exploration on the surface.

The North Pole was conquered by sledge on April 6, 1909 (Peary). Now hardly a day passes but that a weather- or H-bomb carrying-plane flies above it. And the Pole has been reached several times by atomic submarines cruising under the everlasting arctic ice. The South Pole was reached by overland journey on January 18, 1912 (Scott). It is now permanently inhabited, thanks

to air transport as regular and almost as uneventful as flights between the other continents, a by-product of the International
Geophysical Year.

There are great extremes of temperature on the earth's surface.
A temperature of 136 degrees Fahrenheit observed at Azizia,
Tripolitania, in northern Africa, on September 13, 1922, is gen-
erally accepted as the world's highest temperature recorded under

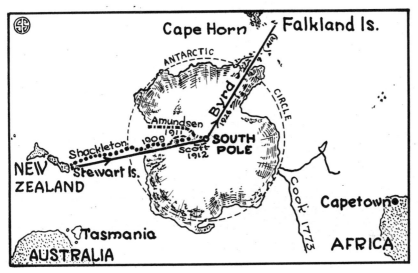

Map of Antarctica.

Captain Robert F. Scott and men at South Pole.

Operation Deep Freeze—Helicopter takes off from U.S. Coast Guard Cutter *Northwind* **while ship breaks ice in Moubray Bay, Cape Hallett, Antarctica, in co-operation with the Navy in support of the International Geophysical Year's Scientific Studies.**

standard conditions. Higher reported temperatures cannot be accepted as official because details on the accuracy and exposure of the thermometer are usually lacking. The lowest temperature ever recorded on the surface was 126.9 degrees below zero Fahrenheit, observed by a Soviet party at their Vostok camp on Antarctica on August 24, 1960. The lowest temperature at the South Pole itself was recorded at 110 degrees below zero Fahrenheit on September 13, 1959. But a temperature of 135.4 degrees below zero Fahrenheit (believed to be a world's record low at any height anywhere) was recorded 13 miles above the South Pole on July 16, 1958, by an airborne instrument launched by the U. S. Weather Bureau.

While the surfaces of the earth—its oceans, plains, valleys, and mountains—have been explored, the hard heart of this globe has not been penetrated. We do not know by direct exploration what lies within the earth. We are not even sure of what lies six miles beneath the ground on which we walk.

A challenging adventure is the piercing of the earth's crust in the interests of geological exploration. Scientists plan to drill a six-mile-deep hole through the crust of the earth to the underlying mantle.

The earth's crust is a thin, slaglike covering of light rocks averaging ten miles in thickness, a mere four hundredth of the earth's radius. Below the crust is a mantle and an inner core. Neither has ever been reached by man.

Willis Jacobs of the Geophysics Division, U.S. Coast and Geodetic Survey raising flag at the South Pole, Dec. 21, 1959.

The mantle accounts for 80 per cent of the earth's volume and is believed to be composed of a material similar to peridotite. The core is thought to be composed of a mixture of iron and nickel.

Between the crust and mantle is a transitional layer known as the Mohorovicic Discontinuity, commonly referred to as the *Moho*. Scientists know of the Moho's existence because seismic waves sent down through the crust undergo an abrupt increase in velocity when they encounter this layer of chemical or physical change.

The exact composition of the underlying mantle is one of the most important unsolved problems of geophysics. The six-mile-deep hole needed to pierce the crust would not be dug on land, because the earth's crust under the continents averages twenty miles in thickness, while under the oceans it averages only five

In the Snow Mine at the South Pole—Glaciologists working in ninety-foot snow mine beneath the South Pole scientific station during the summer season rigged up gauges to study closure rates of the mine's walls over a long span of time.

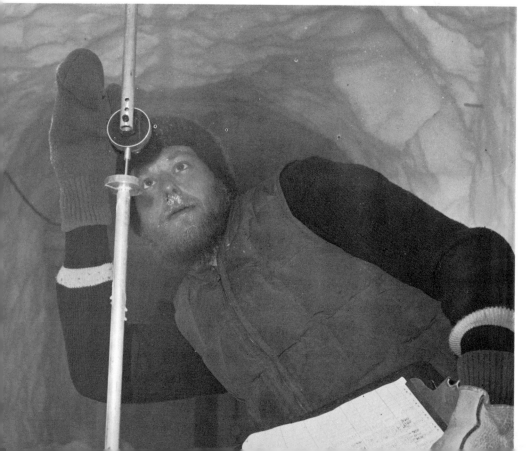

The U.S.S. *Skate* (SSn-578) the second U.S. nuclear-powered submarine to reach the North Pole, on her second visit there on August 17, 1958.

miles. The Moho and mantle are far closer to the surface of the sea than they are to the surface of the land, even allowing for the depth of the ocean, which averages about two and a half miles.

Sampling of the sediments of the ocean floor, the earth's core, the Moho, and the mantle could reveal the nature of marine organisms back through time, perhaps to the origin of life. It could provide clues to the origin and structure of the earth and add meaning to, or confirm, great stores of geological data accumulated during past decades. Sediments could contain an uninterrupted record of the earth's development for two billion years.

The Moho exploration may show that the earth's surface on which we live is moon-stuff. One theory is that some three to four billion years ago the crustal layers of the earth, especially those of the continents, were created by a breakup of the moon, then a solar planet, parts of which were captured by the earth.

This exploration of the earth's interior is one of the great pioneering attempts of the century, rivaling, despite its proximity to the earth's surface, the probing of outer space.

The ocean of air in which we live—the atmosphere—is important because it is our breath of life, it shields us from space radiation, and in it our weather is born and operates.

Weather is of daily concern to everyone. To many industries, such as air transportation, agriculture, and shipping, it is of prime importance to know what to expect meteorologically tomorrow, next week, and even next year, if that is possible.

Paved in diamonds—About 2,-500 diamond stones pave the surface of a core drill crown produced for Project Mohole. The nine-inch-diameter crown will cut a three-and-one-quarter-inch core. This crown contains 786 carats of diamond drill material contributed to Project Mohole by Industrial Distributors Ltd., Johannesburg, South Africa. The unpaved areas of the crown are water channels.

Weather forecasting and recording as a science is only a little more than a century old in this country, going back to Joseph Henry and the early days of the Smithsonian Institution. For many years, until this century was about three decades old, weather was considered largely local and a surface phenomenon. Reliable forecasts were limited to only hours ahead, and there was little wonder that folklore about weather was given credence. Aching corns, signs in the clouds and proverbs, such as "rain before seven, shine before eleven," were relied upon for short-term prognostications. For longer-range forecasts, the bark of trees, bird migrations, and even woolly bear caterpillars were considered prophets.

Two major developments in meteorology have made it possible to extend the time and accuracy of weather forecasting.

One was the introduction of the idea that surface weather is governed by high-altitude winds that move ceaselessly in a globe-girdling belt. The other was the ability to analyze the weather numerically by the use of high-speed computers.

The late Swedish meteorologist, Dr. Carl-Gustaf Rossby, proposed that weather predictions should be made after considering the present state of the atmosphere over the entire Northern

The **CUSS-I** drilling barge—now owned and operated by Global Marine Exploration Co.—was originally developed by the West Coast oil industry for off-shore oil exploration, and has drilled an unmatched total of 200,000 feet of holes in the ocean floor. This uniquely designed vessel off Guadalupe Island applied these techniques in the scientific project Mohole for drilling at unprecedented ocean depths of 12,000 feet.

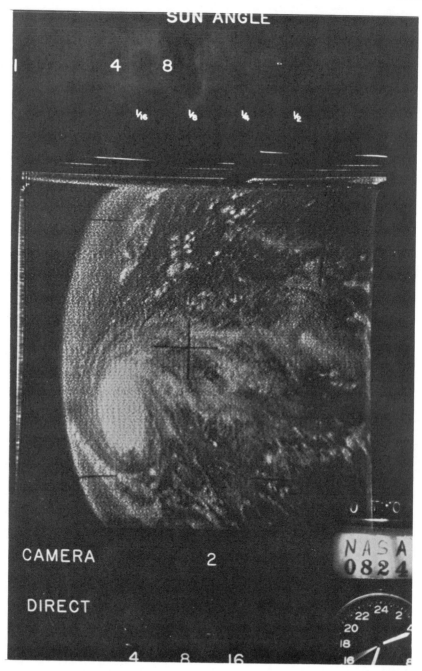

Betsy—Meteorological satellites are leading the way to better weather prediction. Shown here is Hurricane Betsy, photographed east of Hatteras, N.C., by Tiros III. The eye of the hurricane is approximately two hundred miles in diameter.

Hemisphere and the history of its motions for the previous few months.

If the large-scale motions of the atmosphere were made visible by a vast number of free-floating balloons at about twenty thousand feet above the surface, an observer on an earth-circling satellite would soon notice the balloons all drifting eastward relative to the earth.

Looking more closely, such an observer would see that the speed of this westerly current was not the same from pole to pole, but varied slowly with latitude. It would move fastest over the two thousand miles of the temperate zones, or mid-latitudes, becoming much weaker or even reversing its direction over the poles and the equator.

The high-level river of air over the mid-latitudes does not flow in a straight path, but dips north and south as it moves, meandering in much the same way as a stream. Meteorologists call this great meandering current which circles the earth, the planetary wave.

If the satellite observer viewed the myriad balloons floating in the earth's atmosphere even more carefully, he would find a constantly changing series of whirlpools and eddies embedded in the giant river of air.

Continually forming and disintegrating, these whirling air masses are depicted as high- and low-pressure areas on weather maps such as those issued daily by the U. S. Weather Bureau. They also move from west to east in a more or less regular way, at a speed slightly less than the planetary wave.

This regularity is what led first to the art of weather forecasting, then to the now-emerging science of weather prediction. By charting these flow patterns, meteorologists have learned to predict where high- and low-pressure areas will move in the future, based on their repeating patterns known from past motions.

Much more important, however, the atmosphere's regular motions show that air obeys the same laws as other fluids. Using many shortcuts, meteorologists are learning to apply these laws to the atmosphere.

This new knowledge of the physics of the atmosphere, linked with new computation devices, has allowed forecasts for five days in the future so relatively accurate that they became a public service that could be relied upon. Weather for tomorrow and the

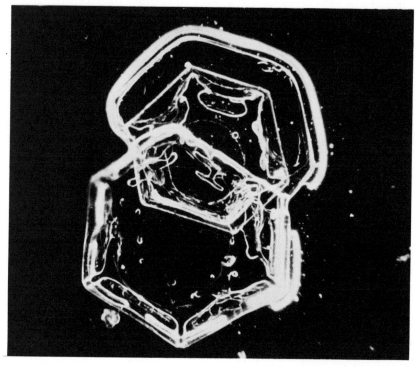

Plastic replicas of ice crystals obtained during artificial rain-making experiments by a team of scientists from the University of Chicago, conducted at Argonne National Laboratory near Lemont, Ill. Due to limitations of magnification possible with an optical microscope, it is impossible to see in this picture whether the ice crystals were formed around silver iodide "seed" particles. However, scientists have demonstrated in laboratory experiments that rain can be induced by injecting silver iodide crystals into a cloud.

day after in any given locality was predicted with great accuracy.

Forecasts for thirty days in the future, issued twice a month, based on numerical weather predictions, are more often right than wrong. They promise to improve as scientists gain more knowledge of how and why world-wide circulation patterns change. A future aim of the meteorologists is to forecast the weather at least ninety days in advance. They cast a speculative eye toward even longer forecasts, realizing that this will take much more work and time. When they dare to apply their methods to the next season or the next year, they will be on the verge of puzzling out what, if anything, is happening to the climate, which may be getting warmer according to observations of glaciers. But this invades the realm of geology rather than meteorology.

Man has always dreamed of controlling the weather. Rain makers attempted to practice their "magic" among primitive people. Even in modern times when droughts came, there were those who claimed to be able to bring rain by such acts as firing a cannon. Sometimes rain did come, but it was probably on the way anyhow.

Scientific attempts at weather modification and controls were taken more seriously since they were based on "seeding" clouds to release rain from saturated clouds in much the same way that it occurs naturally. Dry ice, silver iodide, and water droplets, sprayed from airplanes, were shown in tests to trigger some rain from clouds that were ready to release it. Despite special and localized successes, most experts came to the conclusion that there was no real basis for the belief that the weather or climate of a large portion of the country could be significantly modified by cloud seeding.

It was realized that the energies and extent of storms and atmospheric circulation are so tremendous that no man-applied forces can be expected to modify them. Even the gigantic effects

First man-made snow: Flying in a small cabin plane, Schaefer seeded "supercooled" cloud with pellets of dry ice. A few minutes later, curtains or draperies of snow began falling from the cloud.

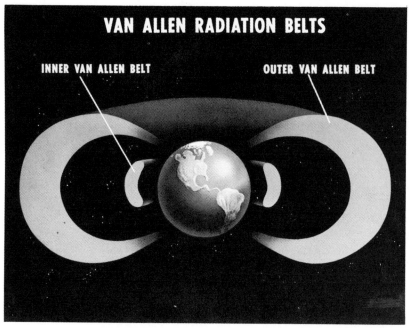

Van Allen Radiation Belts.

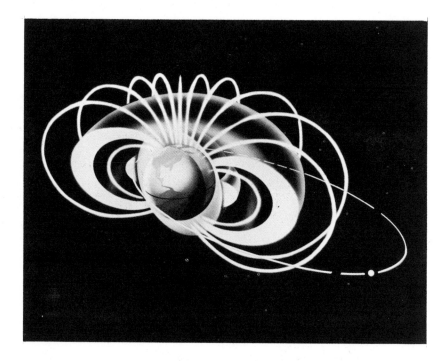

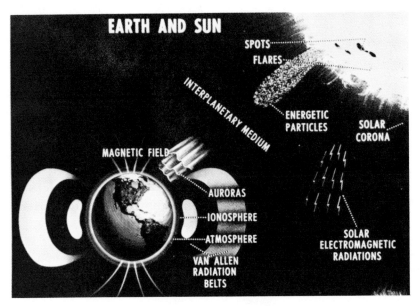

Van Allen Radiation Belts.

of an H-bomb explosion, if it were foolishly used that way, would not change the course of weather materially. This fact did not stop people from blaming weather changes they did not like upon atomic bomb explosions far removed from any possible effect on the area of abnormal weather.

The most far-flung and intensive study ever undertaken of the earth as a planet took place during the International Geophysical Year, which was actually eighteen months long, extending through 1958. This research effort, participated in by sixty-six nations, including the U.S.S.R., was an enlarged repetition of the International Polar Years, the first in 1882 and the second, fifty years later.

The IGY accented Antarctica. That continent was explored intensively and the South Pole colonized for the first time.

Artificial satellites of the earth were put into orbit and outer space probes launched.

Intense bands of unexpected radiation, mysterious in origin, were found to start 250 miles in space, increasing in intensity from there on out to an unknown distance. This radiation may hinder future space travel. Gravity was measured successfully with high accuracy from submarines and, for the first time, from surface ships, giving new information on the constitution and shape of the earth. The atmosphere 200 to 2,000 miles high was proved denser than had been guessed before satellite probing. The sun was found to emit X-rays that cause blackouts of radio communications by generating an additional, electrically ionized layer of the upper atmosphere. The earth holds 40 per cent more snow and ice than was previously believed.

The device of accenting earth research during the IGY promises to have continuing benefits and to inspire more inquiry into the natural conditions upon the globe on which mankind must live. For instance, there was renewed attention to the three-quarters of the planet's area that is water-covered, and this intensified oceanographic research over the years should allow greater use of the high seas for production of food, understanding of weather, and clarification of other unpredictable phenomena.

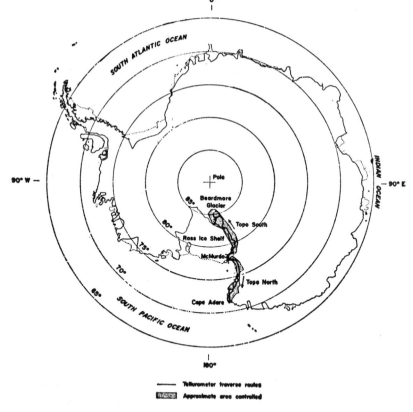

NATIONAL SCIENCE FOUNDATION

100,000-square-mile Antarctic map.

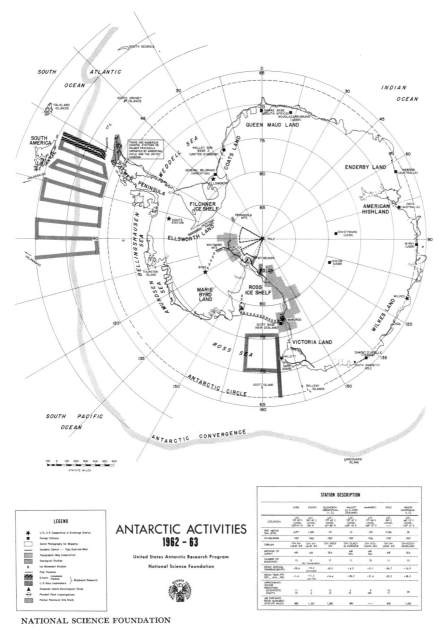

	BYRD	EIGHTS	ELLSWORTH (ARGENTINA-U.S.)	HALLETT (U.S.-NEW ZEALAND)	McMURDO	POLE	WILKES (AUSTRALIA-U.S.)
LOCATION	LAT. 79° 59' S LONG. 120° 01' W	LAT. 75° 15' S LONG. 77° W	LAT. 77° 43' S LONG. 41° 08' W	LAT. 72° 18' S LONG. 170° 19' E	LAT. 77° 51' S LONG. 166° 37' E	LAT. 90° S LONG.	LAT. 66° 15' S LONG. 110° 32' E
FEET ABOVE SEA LEVEL	4,871	1,500	131	16	103	9,186	30
ESTABLISHED	1957	1962	1957	1957	1956	1957	1957
TERRAIN	ON 394-LAND ICE	ON 394-LAND ICE	ON SHELF ICE	ON GLACIAL MORAINE	ON VOL-CANIC ASH	ON 394-LAND ICE	ON ROCKY HEADLAND
METHOD OF SUPPLY	AIR	AIR	SEA	AIR SEA	AIR SEA	AIR	SEA
NUMBER OF BUILDINGS	13	13 (Air Transportable)	17	11	70	11	10
MEAN ANNUAL TEMPERATURE (F°)	-10.4	-12.4 (estimated)	-8.3	+4.2	+0.1	-56.7	+16.9
MEAN TEMP (F°) DEC., JAN., FEB.	+1.6	+11.2 (Jan-Feb)	+16.4	+38.2	+21.6	-25.2	+28.9
APPROXIMATE WINTER PERSONNEL (SCIENTISTS) (NAVY)	11 19	5 6	12 12	6 12	8 185	10 11	20
AIR DISTANCE FROM McMURDO (STATUTE MILES)	885	1,525	1,280	360	-----	830	1,330

STATION DESCRIPTION

ANTARCTIC ACTIVITIES
1962 - 63

United States Antarctic Research Program

National Science Foundation

LEGEND

★ U.S., U.S. Cooperative or Exchange Station
■ Foreign Stations
☐ Aerial Photography for Mapping
▨ Geodetic Control --- Topo East and West
▦ Topographic Map Compilation
▨ Geological Studies
X Ice Movement Studies
↗ Pole Traverse
◢ Eltanin { Completed Planned } Shipboard Research
▲ Roosevelt Island Glaciological Study
◇ Plunkett Point Investigations
▨ Palmer Peninsula Site Study

NATIONAL SCIENCE FOUNDATION

Antarctic activities map.

Humanity has only one earth upon which to live, despite eventual travel to other planets and the very remote possibility of their colonization. The earth is our only home. For this reason alone, this century's accelerated drive to know more about the earth is good planning for the future.

COMMUNICATION

BEFORE THE NINETEENTH CENTURY, the physical transport of written or printed messages—over oceans and plains and mountains, painfully and slowly by sailing ships, by horseback and stage, by human runners—provided the fastest means of communication.

Morse's telegraph and its code of dots and dashes became the first means of almost instantaneous transmission of intelligence, "What hath God wrought!" There followed cables that spanned oceans. Telegraph and railroads grew up together, shortening distance and bringing people always closer together.

What wonder it was when America was celebrating its first century of independence that the human voice, converted into modulated electrical waves, could be transmitted over wires to distant places. Bell's telephone extended one's own neighborhood to amazing distances, and allowed gossip and important talk, alike, to be exchanged between almost all civilized human habitations.

Marconi's wireless, using Hertzian waves, spanned oceans, with the ether as the conducting medium replacing the multiple wires of telegraph, cable, and telephone. Forerunner of radio and television yet unborn, wireless made the sea safer, and the distress calls, CQD and SOS, introduced dramatic chapters of rescue from shipwreck.

The daily press, evolved from the gazettes of earlier days, felt and exercised its power, growing enormously and wielding be-

72

fore the turn of the century political influences it was never again to have. The cry of "Extra!" was not stilled and made obsolete until the advent of radio, with its news bulletins within minutes of the happening of disaster. The linotype had mechanized the setting of the body of newspapers, and with monotype had likewise replaced the hand compositor for the production of books and other printing. Rotary presses rolled out thousands of newspapers an hour. News was distributed nation wide and world wide by wire.

The press in the twentieth century grew with the country and the population, with daily newspapers first multiplying, later consolidating until competition to serve news and purvey advertising gave way toward midcentury to many one-newspaper cities with only radio and TV as rivals.

Magazines achieved gigantic circulations, and their production techniques, utilizing color printing and lithography to the fullest, made possible a blanketing uniformity of editorial and advertising content that brought the remotest hamlet and ranch into the same thought stream as Fifth Avenue, Michigan Boulevard, or Market Street.

Advertising became the strident handmaiden of the entrepreneur. By print in newspaper, magazine, and billboard, by sound

On December 12, 1901, Guglielmo Marconi at a hastily erected receiving station on Signal Hill, St. John's, Newfoundland, was successful in detecting Morse signals emanating from Poldhu in Cornwall, 2,200 miles away. The Atlantic Ocean had been bridged by wireless telegraphy—an achievement which leading scientists of the day had declared to be impossible.

Picture shows Guglielmo Marconi in the room in the old Barracks Hospital, on Signal Hill, St. John's, Newfoundland, with the receiving apparatus he used.

over radio, and by visual appeal over TV, the "sell, sell, sell" of modern business became a science and an art. Psychology was snatched from the universities to work on Madison Avenue, and some of the most careful so-called "research" upon markets was done by advertising agencies bent on merchandising more soap, cosmetics, cigarettes, and purported remedies for what ails mankind. Madison Avenue was even called upon to manage political campaigns, and the slick TV pitch to sell a presidential candidate (like a new detergent) was a modern departure from brass bands and torchlight parades of yesteryear.

Product of photography, the motion picture, coming of age early in the century, arose to world dominion even before it was given voice by a wedding with electronics. The old silent black-and-white variety of movies, lacking the limitations of language, carried with ease entertainment and ideas to all parts of the globe. Actors and actresses became our ambassadors. The good and the bad of our culture became implanted overseas as it gave our own peoples another common denominator.

The phonograph, brain child of Edison, also achieved great universality, carrying 78 rpm music to the millions before radio and electronic turn-tables outmoded the simpler records and brought the 45 or 33⅓ rpm long-play discs into another popular wave of reproduced sound.

The talkies revolutionized the motion picture industry. First, they were a combination of movie and photography, then sound was recorded in gradations of density on film and recreated by photoelectric cells into music and speech. The march of photography gave the movie color, as it was brought to still photographs, even those that anyone can take for himself. Multiple cameras and projectors and at least two microphones and speakers were combined to give the illusion of depth to both color picture and high-fidelity sound. The movie had come alive, recreating with

Thomas A. Edison demonstrated his tin-foil phonograph before the National Academy of Sciences meeting in Washington, D.C., and to President Rutherford B. Hayes at the White House. This portrait was taken at Washington by Mathew Brady, Civil War photographer, in April 1878.

uncanny accuracy the reality of the scenes portrayed. Science and technology expanded the dramatic art.

The electronic twins, radio and television, brought music, entertainment, and information to the masses, developing nationwide networks of stations in the years between the two world wars.

Made possible technically by the vacuum tube in large measure, radio broadcasting served receivers by the millions in living rooms, bedrooms, and kitchens, in automobiles, and even in schools. All this has happened since about 1921. We can all be in touch with what is going on in the world, but we pay for it by being forced to listen to the sponsor's messages.

Television, almost two decades younger than radio, is an adaptation of the physicist's oscilloscope, that converts electrical impulses into pencils of light with which pictures can be painted on the face of a tube. More complicated than radio, it needs more "space" in the electromagnetic spectrum. It costs more to produce and it demands the eyes as well as the ears of its audience. At the price of more complications and more expensive cameras and receivers, color has come to TV. Thus, modern TV has caught up with the movies.

Television broadcasts beamed from airplanes flying six miles up in the air can supply programs to people living within a radius of two hundred miles.

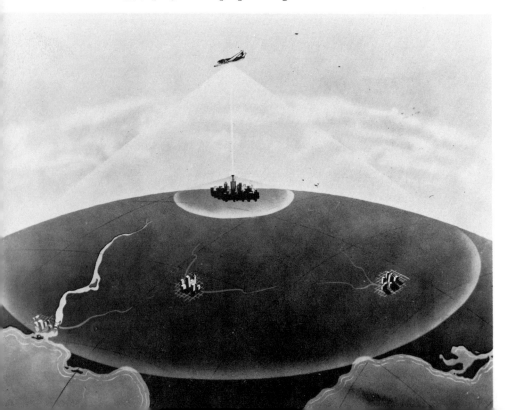

Coaxial cable.

Pictures and facsimile can be transmitted over wires and over radio channels. The principles involved are much the same as in television; light and dark are converted into changes in electrical impulses which are transmitted and then reconstituted. The tempo is slower and the fidelity is greater. Facsimile is replacing the teletypewriters just as those machines made Morse code circuits obsolete. Telephoto circuits span the nation and the oceans, carrying spot photographs to daily newspapers and TV stations.

The gigantic coverage of channels for electrical communication—telephone, radio, telegraph, TV—utilizes the vast expanse

Radar Umbrella, a light portable unit developed especially for beachhead use, is used both as a reflector in sending out shortwave radio pulses and as a receiver to catch wave echoes reflected from enemy targets. The unit's rotating, umbrella-like antenna is shown in the picture.

of the frequency spectrum, the so-called *ether,* as well as special wire and directional beams of radio. The point-to-point communications are generally metallic circuits, although dozens of telephone and telegraph channels can be carried on a four-pair cable. The TV networks use radio beams or coaxial cables, since a single TV program uses the electromagnetic wave space of a multiplicity of telephone, telegraph, or radio channels. Special parts of the radio spectrum are reserved for FM (frequency modulation) radio, including channels used for police, taxi dispatching, air traffic, and mobile telephones on land and sea.

Radar, which sends out radio signals that are bounced back from objects thus detected by the returned signals, played a major role in World War II in spotting attacking airplanes. Radar networks, stretching across the vulnerable parts of the world, are continually alert to discover attacking supersonic bombers and even speedier missiles that might be launched in a sneak attack. Radar born of war still serves defensively, but it has also become a useful civilian tool in the air and at sea to prevent collisions, detect thunderstorms, and chart the landscape.

With the penetration of man-made objects into outer space, the instruments in satellites and rockets send back, by radio teleme-

U.S. Naval Research Laboratory experimental pulse radar transmitter, 1933.

OFFICIAL U.S.N. PHOTOGRAPH

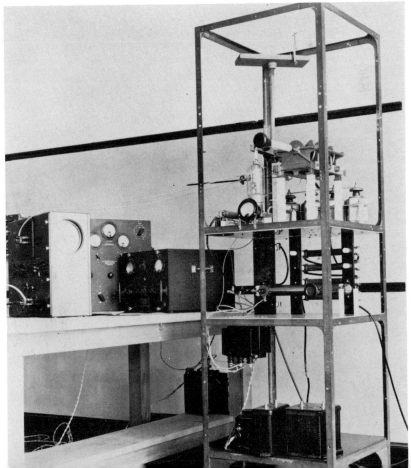

tered signals, information about the conditions in space areas about which we would otherwise never be able to know. The amount of matter in space, the existence of bands of dangerous radiation, the temperature, the intensity of electromagnetic radiation from outer space that cannot penetrate the air of the earth can all be detected. When probes are sent to the vicinity of the moon and the other planets, these robot devices will communicate what they find there by radio and even television.

Written records still constitute the most permanent and time-binding means of communication serving to transmit intelligence, not only currently in communities and nations, but between re-

XAF radar antenna which was installed on U.S.S. *New York* **in 1938 by U.S. Naval Research Laboratory.**

OFFICIAL U.S.N. PHOTOGRAPH

Pioneer microfilm reading machine being used by the author (Watson Davis). Microfilm was developed under the sponsorship of Science Service in the 1930's to make it possible to copy economically material in libraries and place it, upon demand, on the desks of scientists and scholars.

mote peoples and between generations. Libraries and archives, combined with methods for placing their wealth of knowledge at the disposal of those who need it, form the memory of our civilization. Joining the books and journals that were, since the rise of printing, the prime repository of knowledge, there are now new mechanisms for reproducing and distributing the written word. Microfilm, born in the 1930's to place economically the content of libraries on the desks of scholars and scientists, was later adapted to banking records, V-mail, and the preservation of perishable records such as newspapers printed on wood-pulp paper. These reduced-size photographs, magnified for reading when needed or enlarged photographically, are also used to reduce to smaller volume the accelerating bulk of the business and historical files of our record-minded civilization.

For the first time in history, there is some hope of keeping up with the mass of knowledge. In the early days of America there were professors of natural philosophy who took the whole of science as their specialty. In these days the details of science have so proliferated that the specialties have become more and more compressed, with a gigantic increase in the amount of knowledge and the records that contain it. Keeping up with the publication of new research and the synthesis of new with old becomes nearly impossible using the old methods of library classification for books and the multiplex of indices for journals.

The advent of electronic data processing devices, so-called "mechanical brains," gives some hope of marshaling into a sort of world brain the accumulated knowledge of the world. Digital computers were primarily invented to solve problems concerned with the paths of missiles, and other military problems whose resolution by previous methods was too tedious and slow. If it is a question of determining where to aim an anti-missile missile to meet and destroy a rocket-propelled thermonuclear bomb, almost any expenditure of dollars is justified. The whole computer development was speeded lavishly for that reason. By-products, probably as valuable as the military uses, have been machines that will do bookkeeping, mechanize banking, keep personnel records, and incidentally store up, arrange, and reproduce when needed all sorts of information which has been fed into them intelligently. This is the hope of science—not being drowned in a rising tidal wave of facts rolling upon facts.

It is possible to work out methods of filing and retrieving information through use of various breeds of computer-like devices. Much more than mere electronic devices and new-fangled gadgets will be necessary, since sound and novel mathematical methods must be used. But a beginning has been made and, if the world realizes and will finance the need for accessible knowledge, the world brain may emerge. However it is not a simple problem, for it is compounded of semantics, attitudes, philosophies, languages, and modes of thought, as well as the hard-won facts in the voluminous scientific record.

The multiple tongues of the world that are used for the writing of that immense scientific record are an added obstacle. There is a dream of mechanical translation, but this is far from realized. The only translator is still a trained human brain.

The very logical idea of a universal language, that would solve the dilemma of the Tower of Babel, arose most prominently in the last century, and there have been some three hundred attempts to devise such a world tongue. Latin, now dead for science, was an international tongue in the Middle Ages.

The most promising international auxiliary language is what may be thought of as "standard average European," a sort of Latin of the modern world, with regularized grammar, non-inflected construction and a world-usage vocabulary. Called *Interlingua*, it has proved in a few years its usefulness, particularly in abstracts of scientific papers in journals and at congresses. An Interlingua abstract makes the communication available to all who desire what the paper covers, for anyone educated in a Western language can read Interlingua without study. Eventually, it may come to be spoken. Meanwhile, as more and more journals extend their universality by adopting Interlingua for auxiliary summaries, there will be faster and easier interchange of science. Interlingua, because it is so simple and practical, seems destined to realize the hope of Zamenhof for his Esperanto, which sadly in almost a century of existence has not achieved as much scientific practicality as the juvenile Interlingua. From Interlingua's demonstration in the field of science, the vested interests in national languages, each touted by adherents as a possible world tongue, may be subdued sufficiently to allow its application in international, political, and economic affairs. The hundreds of languages of the world will and should continue to exist. Peoples of one tongue must continue to master and appreciate other languages, but within our grasp is the means of universal verbal communication that would do so much to allow understanding between persons and peoples, without which there will be no peace.

An overall view of ENIAC showing machine in process of being prepared to solve a hydrodynamical problem.

THE
AUTOMOTIVE
AGE

THE AUTOMOBILE is much younger than this century as a reliable means of transportation. Remove autos, trucks, and buses from the growing network of roads and highways in the civilized world, and much of life as we know it would be slowed down or come to a grinding halt. Powered by liquid fuel, bountifully supplied by the pools of "black gold" created in past geological eras, these automotive vehicles operate on principles discovered in the last century but brought to application on a large scale only a relatively short time before the First World War.

The automobiles of today throughout the world are predominantly fueled by gasoline, but this was not the case in the early days of the century, during the years when the automobile was being developed. Some of the earlier automobiles were powered by steam. Actually there were vehicles for running along the roads in Europe even before the railroad came into existence.

The internal combustion engine, particularly the four-cycle type invented in 1878 by Dr. Nicholas A. Otto in Germany, supplies the principal motive power for the automobiles of today. Electricity had its technological and fashionable vogue for motive power in the early part of the century, but such cars powered by storage batteries did not survive competition with gasoline power beyond the mid-1920's. Ladies liked them, but the speed was too slow and the batteries had to be recharged every fifty miles or so. There is a chance that the fuel cell, generating electricity from burning gases, may yet return electric cars to the road in this century in a very new form.

There were a number of practical but embryonic automobiles at about the beginning of the century. Most of them still had the lines of the buggies they were replacing. They were called *horseless carriages*. Most had one- and two-cylinder engines. Steering continued to be by a tiller-like arrangement in some cases. Most of the brand names are known only in history, but a few survive today. Most important in the early days were: Duryea, Autocar, Cadillac, Pierce, Olds (the first in mass production), and Ford.

The automobile industry in America came of age with the Oldsmobile and the Ford. The Model T was not Henry Ford's first, but this famous model, appearing in 1908, converted the automobile from a rich man's luxury to the working man's necessity. The Model T was cheap enough ($360 at one time, 1917) so that millions could own it. Ford's first automobile-assembly line for the Model T in 1913 was a significant innovation. By the time the Model A Ford superseded the Model T in 1927, under the impetus of the competition from Chevrolet, Overland, and smaller car manufacturers, more than fifteen million had been

One of millions of Model T Fords that ushered in the automotive age.

manufactured. For ten years, half of all the cars built in America had been Model T's.

The legal and business battles over the Selden patents were almost as influential in shaping the early automobiles as the development of engines, transmissions, brakes, and tires. George B. Selden applied for a patent on an automobile on May 8, 1879, with sweeping claims covering the vehicle as a whole and not merely its internal combustion engine. The patent was finally issued November 5, 1895. Not until 1911, when Ford, who refused to pay a royalty, was held not to have infringed, was auto building free to go forward without patent restraint.

Many of the features of the automobile were pioneered in Europe and brought to America. These included putting the engine up front instead of under the seat where buggy imitation had forced it (it has recently returned to the rear in some small cars), the sliding-gear transmission, the torque converter, and the fluid coupling, which came into use much later although invented in 1902.

Various refinements were incorporated into the automobile to make it more automatic, operationally simpler, and more reliable. Kerosene lamps of the buggy era gave way to acetylene, then to

RESEARCH LABORATORIES, GENERAL MOTORS CORP.

The original Kettering self-starter.

Approaches on harbor drive, Portland, Ore.

electric lights, powered in the beginning by current from the magneto which replaced batteries as a source of ignition. Generators and storage batteries took over a few years before World War I. The electric starter of Charles F. Kettering made hand cranking of the engine obsolete, and had more to do with making cars practical for women than any other improvement. The evolution of the modern automobile was a series of innovations, such as improved carburetors, vacuum- and then pressure-fed fuel, oil pressure systems, tires that were changed by removing tire and wheel as a unit, push-button transmission changing, power brakes, power steering, and a succession of other developments. Horsepower and speeds increased with both engine improvement and better roads.

Through the years, the automobile changed from an imitation of the buggy to an attractive and functional all-weather vehicle. The touring car, open to the elements, was predominant until the 1920's when popularly priced closed cars were introduced. The sedan is the prevalent body-type of automobile but, because of its ability to carry things as well as people, the station wagon has had a continuing vogue. The sports car, of U.S. as well as foreign manufacture, has appeal even though, or because, it can usually carry only two people. In rural areas light trucks double for personal transport and the sturdy "jeep" still conquers less improved roads.

More than two thousand different makes of cars have been manufactured in the United States, but the mortality has been high, so that in a typical mid-century year well over three-quarters of all cars were produced by the top three big manufacturers.

Passenger cars are manufactured at the rate of over five million per year. Through 1958, 139,350,847 cars had been produced, with 56,645,000 registered at that time in the United States. The whole U.S. population could be transported at one time in the operating automobiles—buses and trucks excluded—with empty seats to spare. The number of cars per capita in the United States is far higher than in any other nation; it is 3.2 times that in France, 3.7 times that in England, and 133 times that in the U.S.S.R.

Overshadowing the statistics, impressive as they are, the

Clover-leaf intersection of arterial highways.

Combine harvesting grain, a typical scene that has made America the bread-basket of the world.

changes that the automobile has brought to American living are sweeping and still in progress. America has become decentralized to an amazing extent. It is practical for millions to live as many miles away from work as a horse and carriage could travel in a day at the beginning of the century. Commuting as many as thirty or more miles is not unusual, and a half-dozen to a dozen miles almost the rule. The automblie is the sole means of transport for many millions of the population. In many of the more crowded areas this ease of travel is causing former farm areas between cities to build up, so that suburbanization is almost continuous. Farmers are no longer isolated, although greatly reduced in number because of the nation's industrialization and increase in agricultural production per worker (generated, in large part, by another automotive advance, the tractor). They can zip into town or city quickly in a car, traveling over roads in most cases quite as good as in the city itself.

Pacing the development of the automobile has been the improvement in roads and highways. At the century's beginning most of the paved roads were in cities, and only a few large cities were connected with all-weather passable highways. The mileage of paved roads in 1904, when the first rural road survey was taken, is given as 144. A comparable figure for some sixty years later is about 814,000 miles. Modern cars demand roads that allow routine travel at a mile a minute, a speed that only crack railroad trains had achieved before 1900.

Highways are costly. A four-lane, divided express throughway

Largest shovel uses over fifteen tons of nickel alloy steel—a mammoth stripping shovel, claimed to be the largest self-powered mobile land vehicle ever built. This dipper has a "bite" of 115 cubic yards, can uncover almost fourteen thousand tons of coal a day. In fifty seconds the machine will pick up almost two hundred tons of material, dump it 420 feet away and swing back for the next bite. The Peabody Coal Company, St. Louis, Mo., began operation of this shovel, built by Bucyrus-Erie Company, South Milwaukee, Wisc., at the company's mine site in western Kentucky, in August 1962.

will cost $356,000 to $1,100,000 a mile, and an interchange will cost about $500,000 to $1,500,000, depending upon the terrain. The old dirt roads, that rains turned into mudholes, today must be well-graded and black-topped to allow use through summer and winter in any kind of weather. This, too, takes many dollars, $57,500 to $175,000 per mile.

Signals and other traffic control devices have become necessary to handle the flow of cars and trucks on the nation's roads in and out of cities. Every motorist must today be as alert as the locomotive engineer of previous decades, and his task of guiding his vehicle does not have the aid of the fixed roadbed of the railway.

To do much of the heavy hauling and digging that was once done by horses and men, tractors large and small build our roads, cultivate our farms, and remake the face of the earth. Some of the machines are truly behemoths, weighing many tons and moving tons of earth with each push. Giant agricultural machines perform multiple operations upon many acres of land a day. Important also are the smaller automotive machines used on small farms, for highway maintenance, in construction, and even for cutting the grass on the lawn.

Many of the larger machines are diesel-powered, burning cheaper petroleum fuel, while the farm tractors are mostly kerosene-fed.

The diesel engine was developed for the heavy jobs needing mobile power. It powered ships and tanks in World War II. It has gone to sea in diesel ships, and it has almost driven the steam locomotives off the rails of the nation. Many buses and heavy trucks, which compete with the railroads, are also diesel powered.

AMERICAN TRUCKING ASSOCIATION

Truck powered by a diesel engine.

Trucks haul an increasing part of the freight of the nation, particularly the lighter loads and those that go to points not served by railroads. Buses are taking passenger traffic from the railroads, and connect towns that the railroads have abandoned or have never served. As the airplane has done on the long passenger hauls, the buses give the railroads stiff competition for passengers on the shorter runs. The contest between airplanes and ships over ocean routes, and buses and railroads over land lines, is somewhat analogous.

For heavy freight, the railroads must still do the job, since the average freight car carries nearly twice as much tonnage as the the largest truck that is usually allowed to use the highways, whose pavements take a beating when the truck burden is too heavy. The comparative loads are 42 tons to 27.6 tons.

The internal combustion engine, and the other liquid-fuel power plants, have made power packages mobile and given our times

Greyhound Scenicruiser powered by a diesel engine.

Rivals: Newest in coal-burning steam locomotives at left, in oil-consuming diesel locomotives at right. Both belong to the Baltimore and Ohio Railroad.

prodigiously plentiful energy where and when it is needed. The internal combustion engine—the automotive vehicles that it powers and the roads that it has demanded—has revolutionized movement on the face of the earth, just as in airplanes it has conquered the air.

AVIATION'S
SPEEDING
PROGRESS

To AN AMAZING EXTENT those who travel today are air-borne. The world has shrunk in its time dimension so much that London is a mere half-dozen hours from New York, Tokyo twelve hours from San Francisco, and the scheduled air travel time around the world is about fifty-four hours.

These are five hundred to six hundred miles-per-hour jet times, but even on shorter hops between cities nearer to each other, the airplane, largely propeller-driven, has brought a telescoping of transport. It is not remarkable to spend the day in a city hundreds of miles away and nonchalantly return home for dinner, as commuters of the air age.

Airplanes carry armies that rain down by parachute upon distant territory. Bombers, until superseded by intercontinental rocket missiles, were ready to deliver across oceans thermonuclear warheads of great destructive power almost at the flash of a fateful signal.

The sound barrier was broken in October 1947. The jet planes of war routinely achieve more than supersonic flight, approaching speeds twice that of sound, nearly Mach 2, a matter of 1,100 miles per hour. They travel immense distances, at intervals sucking in fresh fuel from tanker escorts flying alongside. Air Force bombers have reached speeds upward of 2,000 miles per hour.

Precise instruments guide and navigate the flying craft, with

94

Wilbur Wright

Orville Wright

little touch of human hands except to set the problems to be solved mechanically.

For mail and for urgent cargo, planes are taking over from the slower surface modes of transport, boats and railroads, with forecasts that there will be only one sort of first class mail for the future, that by air. Even freight of the heavier sort is lifted aloft and borne over mountains and valleys, sometimes where a highway or a railroad never has been built and never will exist. The new freighting mode was pioneered because of war requirements. The parts of the world opened to settlement since aviation came of age leaped directly into the air era from dog sledge, pack horse, or human bearers.

The airplane is the first mode of transport over land that achieved freedom from a permanent path upon the surface of the earth. Only a landing field or strip is needed to connect one point or locality with any other part of the earth, the ocean of air providing the means for the relatively small vehicle to journey so blithely. Contrasted with the bulk of railway vehicles and ships necessary for speed, economy, and convenience, the airplane is light, swift, and inexpensive for light hauls of passengers and, even, goods.

Before the twentieth century, man had not flown in the kind

of aircraft that has conquered the air with such effect—the heavier-than-air airplane. The biplane of forty-foot wing-span, which Wilbur and Orville Wright built and which was flown for twelve seconds on the cold morning of December 17, 1903, at Kitty Hawk, North Carolina, was "the first in the history of the world in which a machine carrying a man had raised itself by its own power into the air in full flight, and sailed forward without reduction of speed, and had finally landed at a point as high as that from which it started," to use the words in which Orville Wright described the achievement. It was the beginning of practical aviation.

The Wright brothers discovered the principles of human flight, the aerodynamic laws that were utilized in their gliders and their primitive wind tunnel before they built the successful motor-driven machine. Others had worked upon the problem of human flight before the Wrights: Sir Hiram Maxim, Alexander Graham Bell, Thomas Alva Edison, Samuel Pierpont Langley, Otto Lilienthal, and Octave Chanute. After the Wrights had made their demonstration and the news slowly became known, others built airplanes and engines to drive them. While the Wright brothers were attempting to commercialize their great invention, airplanes made by Santos-Dumont and Blériot made short but successful

Side view of the original Wright aeroplane near Kitty Hawk, N.C., 1903.

Left: Orville Wright in his aeroplane. Right: Boeing B-47 in take-off tests.

flights in France. The early exhibitions of the practicality of flying were climaxed by demonstrations by Wilbur in France and by Orville in America. The year 1908 was an eventful one for the beginning of aviation, for among the flights were those of Orville at Ft. Myer, Virginia, which launched the development of aviation by the United States government. It was a contract with the Army's Signal Corps that provided the incentive for the first military plane carrying a passenger.

For the next half dozen years, until the outbreak of World War I, the progress of airplane building and flight was a series of demonstrations at fairs and expositions, coupled with the use of these flying machines for sport, largely by those wealthy enough to afford the machines and often the hire of pilots to fly them.

War changed the nature of aviation, and the airplane soon gave the world a new and mighty weapon. The Germans used Zeppelin dirigibles, lighter-than-air airships, for their raids on England, but their lack of maneuverability and low altitude soon

Curtiss NC-4 (1919). Left front view on beach.

made them vulnerable to attack by airplanes. Allied air power was used against German industrial centers and even to bomb the Zeppelin works at Friedrichshafen.

The exploits of First World War pilots dramatized the airplane. Shortly afterward, there was a slowly growing realization that aviation could aid peacetime living as well. Using surplus airplanes sold by the government, many young flyers who had fought in the air during the war gave barnstorming exhibitions of flying. Thousands among the curious audiences had their first airplane rides of a few minutes at county fairs or traveling carnivals.

Commercial aviation had not yet been born. But the air services of the Army and the Navy realized that the progress of military aviation would be aided by demonstrations of the usefulness of airplanes in peace. They showed what airplanes could do. The flight of the NC-4, the Curtiss Flying Boat, across the Atlantic with a crew of six was the first air trip between the New and the Old Worlds. Later in 1919, John Alcock and Arthur Whitten Brown made the first nonstop crossing of the Atlantic from St. John, Nfld., to Ireland's west coast, almost 2,000 miles away. Still later in 1919, the first transcontinental airway across the United States was developed to make possible a transcontinental air race won by a round trip of nine days, four hours, and twenty-five minutes. The foundation for commercial aviation was

Alcock and Brown taking off from Newfoundland (Vickers Vimy Rolls-Royce Eagle MK VIII Engines). Left side view from below.

De Havilland DH-4 (modified). Seventy of these aircraft (twenty equipped for night flying) were used on the transcontinental route at Omaha, Neb., July 1, 1924.

laid by such exploits. In 1920, the American speed record was 178 miles per hour. In 1922, the world's altitude record was more than 6½ miles. Army fliers made an exciting adventure-filled around-the-world flight in 1924, a distance of over 26,000 miles covered in about fifteen days. The air conquest of the two ends of the earth was made a few years later, the North Pole being flown over in 1926 and the South Pole reached in 1929.

Even before World War I was ended in 1918, commercial aviation came of age through the beginning of airmail service. Signal Corps pilots and planes inaugurated transport of airmail between Washington, Philadelphia, and New York City. Later the Post Office began flying the mail with its own pilots and its own planes. The time-saving advantages of flying such short distances were not sufficiently great to be as attractive as for longer distances. Late in 1918, hazardous flights between New York and Chicago were undertaken, and two years later a regular air-train service across the continent was begun between New York and San Francisco. In those early days, flying at night proved too hazardous. Not until the first transcontinental lighted airway was constructed between Chicago and Cheyenne, Wyoming, in 1923, was airmail flying attempted at night. The improvement of airways, lighted and serviced with beacons by the government, as well as

Lindbergh's Plane (Ryan NYP) *Spirit of St. Louis* **at Omaha, Neb.**

SMITHSONIAN INSTITUTION

A veteran of 8.5 million air miles—Douglas DC-3.

the building of thousands of airports, had occurred as a result of the growth of commercial aviation by 1929, largely stimulated by the requirements of the early attempts at airmail transport.

No achievement gave the public a greater thrill than the non-stop flight by Charles A. Lindbergh in a single-motor airplane from Roosevelt Field, Long Island, to Le Bourget Field in Paris. Following the Lindbergh flight, there were many attempts at new records. The stimulation of prizes and the fame of transoceanic records helped pioneer flight to distant portions of the earth. Up to this point in the progress of aviation, most of the planes were those that had been developed during the war or small craft primarily built for private flying.

Because of the necessity of military development, the principal nations of the world, the United States among them, organized aeronautical research on an increasing scale. The National Advisory Committee for Aeronautics, from its formation during World War I until it was superseded by the National Aeronautics and Space Administration in 1958, laid the scientific and technological foundation of aeronautics. Working closely with the commercial airplane and aeronautical engine builders, its research established not only the basis for commercial planes but for war planes as well. The first all metal monoplane, the Ford tri-motor, was supplanted by other transports, notably the DC-3 which became a workhorse of the airlines. Radial, air-cooled en-

B-58 Bomber.

gines were developed for the DC-3 and later planes, automatic pilots came into use, landing gears were made retractable, superchargers allowed the planes to fly higher, and flaps on the wings permitted slow speeds on take-off and landing. One of the advances of those days made by NACA research was an increase in the aerodynamic efficiency of the airplane through reduced drag by placing a cowling around the engines and putting them, in part, within the thickness of the wing itself. This innovation, alone, allowed an increase in speed at no large additional cost. The variable pitch propeller, a later development, gave control over the speed of the airplane by varying the bite of the blade without changing the revolutions per minute of the engine, also acting as a brake in landing.

Research continued at an accelerating rate with the dual objective of improving airplanes for peace and war and providing the technological basis for the transition from planes to rockets.

For instance, making fuselages waistlike through development

Airliner Jet Transport, Convair 880.

Douglas DC-8 Airliner.

A scientist at Langley Research Center of NASA inspects a research model of a supersonic transport which could cruise at speeds between 1,500 and 2,000 m.p.h.

of what was called the area rule, an NACA research achievement announced in 1955 but performed earlier, produced 25 per cent more supersonic speed for U.S. military planes. Research and the apparatus for performing it, including wind tunnels, left the range just beyond the speed of sound, achieved during World War II, and invaded ever faster realms. In addition to the aerodynamic problems of the supersonic, still faster speeds required new techniques for withstanding the heat that frictional rush of air at higher speeds generates. New alloys were needed to remain strong at temperatures of thousands of degrees. Cooling that must be carried, although costly in weight, had to be added to keep the pilots alive and functioning, while higher and higher altitudes were tried to avoid some of the barriers set up by the atmosphere.

While the jet passenger age, supplying transportation at just below the speed of sound, was taking over the long hauls around the world, it was recognized that airliners could be designed and built in a few years that would travel three times the speed of sound (Mach 3). If military planes had done it, then passenger craft could follow successfully, although not by simple direct adaptation. These two-thousand-miles-per-hour passenger liners should not be expected before about 1970. The friction heat alone, which would raise the outer surfaces of a Mach 3 liner to 570 degrees Fahrenheit, would require expensive cooling and insulation.

In 1960 a jet liner cost $5,000,000, contrasted with about $800,000 for a DC-6 propeller liner a little over a decade before. The Mach 3 liner would bear a price tag of about $20,000,000. Still, it promises a future when travel time between the two coasts will be as little as one and a half hours.

Airplanes need airfields and, in the case of jets, increasingly long runways in order to take off and land. The great value of planes lies in traveling long distances at high speeds. Even before the airplane was invented, man had long desired to fly like a bird and hover, which an airplane cannot do. Aircraft that can go slowly, rise straight up, and land vertically has been a develop-

The rocket-engine-powered X-15 made its public debut in October 1958.

U.S. AIR FORCE

U.S. Air Force helicopter—the *Work-Horse*.

ment somewhat independent of the conventional airplane. The
first helicopter seems to date from 1907 when a Frenchman
named Cornu flew his craft at a height of one foot. But rotating-
wing aircraft went into service in 1923, when La Cierva demonstrated his autogyro. This breed of aircraft went to work carrying
mail between airfields and downtown post offices in a number
of cities. World War II found the helicopter coming of age and
of great usefulness. Igor Sikorsky was especially identified with
its development. Capable of rising directly upward and hovering
as well as traveling laterally, the helicopter with its whirling
propeller-like wings serves for short hauls of passengers and
cargoes. For rescue at sea and in rough terrain, helicopters are
crafts of mercy. As adjuncts to military operations, they team

**One of the first test pick-ups from rubber life raft using Vickers Helicopter,
1945. (*Right*)**

Special mobile vehicle for transporting and raising and lowering the Navy's XFY-1 Convair Vertical Takeoff Fighter Plane permits the plane to be tilted for easier maintenance.

VTOL-Tri-Service Transport—Artist's conception shows how the XC-142, being designed for the Army, Navy and Air Force by Ling-Temco-Vought, might look as it takes off vertically, later to fly horizontally in the usual manner.

with planes and rockets in the air, and jeeps, trucks, and tanks on the ground.

Development is underway of other aircraft that are able to take off and land, as helicopters do, in very limited space. The VTOL (Vertical Take Off and Landing) craft are airplanes, other than helicopters, that take off and land vertically. The STOL (Short Take Off and Landing) is a craft which requires only a short runway to get into the air. Such a device, when combined with a small automobile-like road car, would become a flying car capable of traveling on the earth and in the air.

The development of aircraft is by no means finished. Combinations of passenger-carrying rockets, which can travel outside the atmosphere but use wings to land through the earth's blanket of air, have been suggested and may materialize when the need for them arises.

ROCKETS
AND
SPACE

ROCKET MISSILES can carry thermonuclear bombs from continent to continent, and can venture into outer space to the moon and beyond. These are creations of the post-World War II part of the century, but their lineage goes back to ancient times when, as tradition has it, the Chinese used Roman candles to frighten horses during their interminable civil wars.

British troops, when they were conquering India a couple of hundred years ago, ran into an annoying kind of fiery weapon that flew into their faces under its own power—rockets made of bamboo.

They adopted this weapon and encased it in iron, producing the Congreve rocket, a famous weapon of the Napoleonic era. These were the missiles that echo in our national anthem, as "the rockets' red glare."

But the real rocket age was theoretically born in the experiments of Dr. Robert H. Goddard in the United States between the two World Wars. His developments, revealed to the world in patents, were applied by the Germans. Their sensational V-2 rockets, that bombarded London, came close to being a decisive weapon. Neglected by the United States, rockets came into military ascendancy only after the Germans staked their military fortunes upon them, expending the same kind of extreme resources upon them that the United States gave to the atomic bomb. The German gamble came close to winning. A little more punch and

110

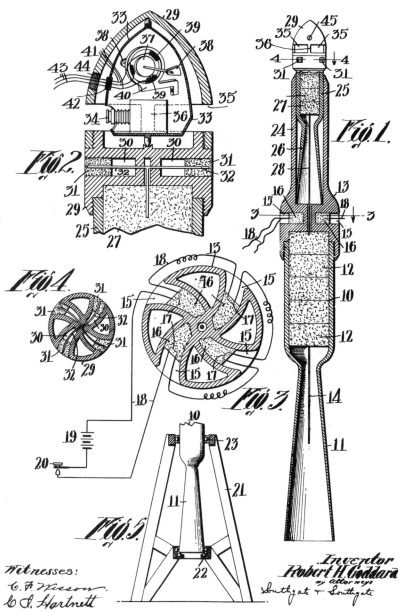

Robert H. Goddard's Rocket Apparatus, patented July 7, 1914.

Rocket launching tower of R. H. Goddard at Roswell, N.M., 1936.

less dissension among the Nazis and the ending would have been different. With the German military collapse, both the victorious Americans and Russians acquired by capture and adoption experts and know-how that put them in the rocket race. The two most potent powers soon created their own versions of intercontinental ballistic missiles and poised them in opposition, ready to hurl the atomic and hydrogen bombs that they both had developed.

Without the military motives and without the necessity of

threats and counter-threats, astronautics might have advanced along peaceful lines but at a much slower pace. The billions for defensive potential offense would have been lacking.

The first rockets ready for war use and intended for space exploration depended upon chemical propulsion systems, mainly liquid oxygen and kerosene. The structural materials for these craft have been markedly improved, their design has been well developed, and manufacturing methods have also seen major advances. The rocket itself has achieved flight stability, even though there is not always complete success in all launchings due to the extreme complexity of the mechanisms and the fact that the failure of a relatively minor part sometimes results in the

Robert H. Goddard in laboratory at Roswell, N.M., 1936.

PHOTOGRAPH BY AUTHOR (WATSON DAVIS)

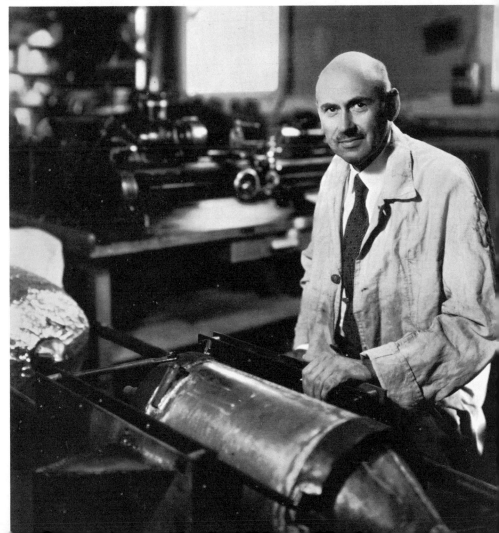

The third-stage rocket accompanying Soviet satellite Sputnik through space recorded by George T. Keene of Rochester.

loss of a rocket. Reliability is one of the most important factors in the rocket program because, if the equipment sending a war rocket on its way or a space rocket into a distant flight fails, the whole intricate and costly endeavor will be in vain. Keeping the relatively small amounts of equipment working for many months without servicing and human attention is necessary if space flights are to be productive and reliable.

With gyroscopic instruments of almost incredible accuracy and reliability available, the problem of guidance of both war rockets and space rockets seems to be much less critical than it was in the early days of development. Communication between space vehicles and stations on the earth is quite easy and reliable to maintain during flights of satellites around the earth or toward the moon and the planets. Eventually propulsion systems not dependent upon chemicals will be successfully devised so that flights in space will be self-powered, rather than dependent almost wholly upon the initial thrust received from the launching power, perhaps with corrective spurts from chemical rockets aboard the

V-2 Rocket. (*Left*)

Major components of the Tiros III weather satellite spread beneath the satellite itself as an inspector checks the individual parts at the RCA Astro-Electronics Division in Princeton, N.J.

vehicle. With the taming of atomic power in the future, rockets will benefit from new methods of power supply. While that which is to come can be forecast with some confidence, the future still is the future. It may never arrive in the shape that our predictive sense imagines.

The greatest impact of space exploration has been upon the minds, the hopes, and the fears of mankind. When the first satellite was launched by Soviet scientists on October 4, 1957, there was immediate and profound realization that man could conquer space. The effect was far greater than the Wrights' first airplane flight. With succeeding space successes, there came more satel-

Perfect launch—Smoke and flame gush from an Atlas rocket as it boosts a Mercury capsule into space.

Atlas rockets into Florida sky—The launching of an Atlas intercontinental ballistic missile from U.S. Air Force Missile Test Center at Cape Canaveral, Fla., where Convair, a division of General Dynamics Corp., is testing this country's first ICBM, Jan. 10, 1958.

lites by American as well as Soviet efforts, a hit upon the moon, the creation of artificial planets of the sun, despite their minuteness. These had elevating effects upon the confidence and the expectations of people in the conquest of space.

The extraordinary future of space exploration has become evident, even discounting, for the moment, its military weapon aspects. Rockets take scientific instruments outside the earth's atmosphere and beyond the earth's magnetic field, answering some of the moot questions about the nature of the planetary system and even of the universe. Direct exploration of the other planets and other parts of the solar system will be undertaken first by instruments rather than by human beings, although eventually there will be Columbuses of space. Men will be on the moon by 1970 or earlier, and they will be both Russians and Americans. Mars will be reached in this century.

The earth is viewed from satellites to chart the clouds, and keep watch upon what is happening on distant parts of the earth. Satellite observations are routinely used in weather forecasting. Watching the march of weather from above the atmosphere brings meteorologists information they need to understand more adequately the ways of the weather and perhaps even to control it. Satellites have become relay points for radio and television, giving us new channels in the electromagnetic spectrum for use in communication between the peoples of the earth. A family of communication satellites, the first of which were Echo, Relay, and Telstar, are permanent additions to the planet's "moons" and our world communication network. From space, the earth can be inspected regularly to prevent dangerous, illicit military maneuvers, but this advantage may be countered by a nation that succeeds in launching nuclear weapons from secret bases remote in space.

If the atomic bomb and more particularly the hydrogen bomb had not been developed, the rocket missiles that span the continents would have been much less attractive from a military standpoint. The cost and the trouble of having rockets carry loads of conventional explosives would probably have made them uneconomical for military use. Hydrogen warheads and ICBM's

Orbit calculator—Computer flight control center is used in plotting all orbits and in making orbital predictions for satellites. Located at Goddard Space Flight Center near Greenbelt, Md., this "nerve center" also records Mercury manned flights.

have a malignant symbiotic relationship. How much further both rockets and atomic weapons need to be developed in order to have them deemed powerful enough by the most eager and aspiring general is uncertain. The factor deciding whether they will be used in future warfare is, in all probability, not astronautical but psychological. An amazing balance of far-flung detecting devices and anti-missile missiles, that can destroy an attacking rocket in the twinkle of a radar pip, promotes a technologic stalemate which may be helpful in keeping the peace.

Ever since Galileo looked at the moon through his telescope, men have dreamed of flying to the moon. Only in this century has there been any expectation that these dreams would come true. That master of science fiction, Jules Verne, had his band of scientists aiming at the moon, not with rockets but with gigantic artillery. The trouble was, of course, that Verne did not know the physics that was discovered by the rocket pioneers years after his success at forecasting, in broad outlines, a future which in many respects is still to be achieved.

Over-all view of Astronaut John H. Glenn, Jr., as he commences entrance into spacecraft, Friendship 7, prior to MA-6 launch operations.

NASA

Cape Canaveral, Fla.—Astronaut John H. Glenn, Jr.'s spacecraft, Friendship 7, being brought alongside recovery ship after world orbital flight.

At Cape Canaveral, Fla., the giant Saturn rocket is serviced by a 185-foot gantry made up of 2,800 tons of steel.

Credit should be given to the rocket pioneers for their preoccupation with, not so much intercontinental bombing, but trips into interplanetary space or, more modestly, means of reaching high altitudes closer to earth that were unattainable otherwise. Scientific experimentation and studies in the upper reaches of the atmosphere were most attractive to Goddard in his early experiments, although he was in charge of the relatively unappreciated rocket research during World War I. Goddard in the 1920's and 1930's was responsible for the chief American effort in space flight. In 1926 he conducted the first successful test of a liquid fuel rocket. Early work was also done in Germany by Hermann Oberth, beginning in the 1920's. Government-sponsored rocket research programs were established in Germany about 1930, the Soviets got in the rocket race about 1934, while serious United States participation did not occur until 1942, despite the early work of Goddard. The birthplace of the intercontinental military rocket and, therefore, also of the space rocket can be said to be the German rocket proving ground at Peenemünde.

The principles of rocket or jet propulsion go back to the seventeenth century and Sir Isaac Newton who expressed the three laws of motion:

1. A body remains at rest or in a state of motion in a straight line unless acted upon by an external force.

2. A force acting upon a body causes it to accelerate in the direction of the force, the acceleration being directly proportional to the force and inversely proportional to the mass of the body.

3. To every action, there is an equal and opposite reaction.

The third law is basic to jet propulsion. The action is a stream of escaping mass, gas created by burning fuel. The reaction created drives the vehicle onward. Unlike an airplane propeller, it does not need air to push against. The jet operates in a vacuum or airless outer space, and this makes the rocket capable of space propulsion. The rocket, of course, must carry its own oxidizer as well as fuel, whereas the jet engines of airplanes use the oxygen of the air.

Newton's law of gravitation, like his laws of motion, is also basic to space operations. There is a mutual attraction, or *pull* be-

ANNA—Artist's conception showing the ANNA geodetic satellite launched from Cape Canaveral. Its purpose is to mark positions on earth, locate the center of the earth's mass, measure the strength and direction of the earth's gravitational field. The satellite is a cooperative venture of the three services and NASA.

tween all particles of matter, from the largest star to the smallest atom. The strength of their gravitational attraction is dependent on their masses and varies inversely as the square of the distance between them; that is, the closer the two bodies are to each other, the greater their mutual attraction.

These facts about gravity make understandable why satellites do not fall from their orbits, and space probes continue to travel after their power is exhausted.

To leave the earth on space exploration missions, a vehicle must overcome the pull of earth's gravity. This can be done by accelerating the vehicle to a given speed. Since the force of the earth's gravity declines with distance from the earth's center, the minimum speed required to overcome gravity varies. At or near the earth's surface, the speed required to overcome gravity is slightly more than seven miles a second, or 25,000 miles per hour. At an altitude of 500 miles from the surface, the requirement

Saturn rocket—World's most powerful known booster, generating a 1,-
300,000-pound thrust, stands poised on the launching pad.

drops to 23,600 miles per hour, and at 5,000 miles altitude it is only 16,630 miles per hour.

The minimum speed at which an object overcomes gravity is known as *escape velocity. Escape,* however, does not mean that the object is forever free from the earth's gravitational influence; it means only that the object or vehicle will not be pulled back to the surface, even when its power is exhausted.

A vehicle having achieved escape velocity does not continue moving at that speed after power exhaustion. Gravity will exert a braking influence and the vehicle will gradually lose speed. It will, however, always have enough momentum to continue moving away from the earth until the control of the sun's gravity predominates over that of the earth.

At a speed lower than that of escape velocity, a vehicle can counterbalance the earth's gravity. For instance, assume that a vehicle is launched into a horizontal path at an altitude of three hundred miles. Since it is above the restraining effect of the atmosphere, it will continue to move at its original speed. It will be

Future lunar spacecraft.

Moon craft—Ranger I, first of a series of lunar spacecraft, is shown being tested at the Jet Propulsion Laboratory, Pasadena, Calif. Ranger will place scientific instruments on the moon.

subject to two forces: 1. The centrifugal, or outward force generated by its speed. 2. The downward pull of the earth's gravity. If, at three hundred miles altitude, the original speed is eighteen thousand miles per hour, the net effect of these two pulls would be zero. One would counterbalance the other. The vehicle or object would be in "continuous fall," its path of movement exactly matching the curve of the earth. It would remain in that state indefinitely if it did not encounter other resistance and would continue to move about the earth at the same speed and altitude. It would then be "in orbit."

For space exploration by rockets which came to fruition in the fifties, the vehicles used were those primarily developed for military purposes. The "hardware" of the ICBM (Intercontinental Ballistic Missile) is well adapted to putting satellites into orbit,

Future space travel to the moon.

impacting landing instruments on the moon and even on Venus and Mars, exploring the atmosphere of Jupiter by means of instruments, and even placing a man or men in satellite orbit around the earth for recovery after a few days of flight. This, of course, is only the beginning because the desire to explore more thoroughly the solar system (and even outside the solar system in future decades), as well as the continuing military race, will bring forth increasingly powerful rocket engines capable of carrying larger and larger payloads into space.

The flight mechanisms for space exploration did not come automatically as a result of military developments, although both peaceful and military advances were made together. There was one prime difference. For war, missiles do not need to make a round trip while, for manned flights into space, the vehicle must be capable of returning to earth safely and reliably.

Space exploration was launched with the first satellite. Its progress promises to be as rapid as the rise of aviation. This century will not see human migration to the moon and other planets. This may never happen.

What occurs in space may dominate the earth, because existing intercontinental missiles use outer space, and satellites by the dozen will never be absent from our sky—watching over us, providing new facilities for our use, and perhaps poising dangers of death and destruction.

Views of the earth from above the atmosphere and its clouds can supplement what can be observed from the surface. Navigational beacons for travel on and above the earth can be installed in satellites. Radio, TV, and communication signals bounce off special man-made "moons" to augment the crowded electromagnetic radio spectrum and, thus, contract still further the informational togetherness of the world.

To aspiring world dictatorship, space can provide the launching pads of H-bombs or worse weapons.

From space may come potential interference with our elaborate warning systems guarding against missile sneak attacks.

The whole world can be watched continuously and instantly for dangerous military developments. International inspection would be preferable to great powers on a space prowl against each other, but even separate nations doing their own space spying could serve to keep an uneasy peace.

Rockets may carry passengers, mail, and freight from point to point on the earth's surface, combined with aeronautical vehicles that allow them to land safely through the heat-generating atmosphere. This application may prove as important as more venturesome outer space travel.

CHEMISTRY—
ELEMENTS AND
MOLECULES

MAN'S UNDERSTANDING of the elements and the materials made from them does not extend very deeply into the past. Until nearly the beginning of the twentieth century, the ancient idea of elements—air, fire, and water—seemed almost understandable and logical. But the chemical revolution that was to have such an industrial effect and so great an influence upon war and peace was in the making as the century began.

Much, but not all, of the chemical progress of the nineteenth century was in the field of inorganic chemistry. Out of applied chemistry came such important industrial processes as the vulcanization of rubber by Charles Goodyear, the electrolytic production of aluminum by Charles Martin Hall, the making of collodion by J. Parkers Maynard, the making of celluloid by I. S. and J. W. Hyatt, the invention of carborundum by Edward Goodrich Acheson, and the production of alloyed high-speed steels by Frederick Winslow Taylor and Maunsel White.

Until the First World War, America followed Europe in most chemical endeavor. The era of organic chemistry, ushered in by Wöhler's synthesis of urea in Germany in 1828, made it necessary as well as fashionable for American chemists prior to 1914 to do their graduate work in Germany if they were to have advanced chemical knowledge and prestige.

Chemistry came into its own in America after World War I. America had to rely upon itself after the debacle of Germany, following a war which was to a large degree made possible by German chemical successes.

Historians may overlook the fact that the German Kaiser would hardly have dared risk war if Fritz Haber had not extracted nitrogen from the air for explosives, food, and other manufactures. Nitrogen was painfully short in Germany, and the possibility of obtaining it from the air we breathe gave the German rulers unfortunate courage. N, for nitrogen, was in a sense the chemical symbol of the First World War.

Forced to become self-reliant by the lack of German dyes, explosives, pharmaceuticals, and other organics, the American chemical industry arose from rudimentary beginnings and ceased being subservient to European chemical "Kultur."

With a similar symbolism, U stands for the Atomic Age ushered in during World War II, U for uranium from which the atomic fission bomb is derived.

Similarly H for hydrogen symbolizes the fusion H-bomb era, which is expected to give rise to thermonuclear power plants that will replace the atomic fission reactors, themselves by-products of the atomic bomb.

H and C are the symbols for the elemental ingredients in the host of new and old hydrocarbons and other chemicals from coal, petroleum, and farm products that give birth to so many industrial, medical, and luxury wonders.

With all the advances in chemistry, the materials of the world are elementally almost the same as in cave-man days, although many of the elements utilized today were unknown and unrecognized. The form, availability, and location of elements have changed.

In a very few instances, as with elements and isotopes transmuted in A-bombs and reactors, small but significant amounts of new kinds of matter have become available to us.

The parade of chemical elements has now reached number 103, far beyond the 92 (with gaps below) of pre-atomic energy days. More elements are certain to be discovered, but more important will be the production and utilization of some of the chemical elements (hafnium, for instance), virtually unknown or unavailable before 1939.

To our knowledge of the inner structure of matter, giant accelerators or atom smashers have added an amazing array of par-

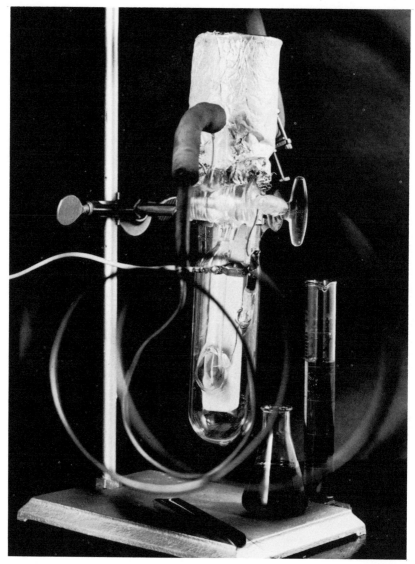

E. I. DU PONT DE NEMOURS & CO.

Frozen free radical chemistry—When chemical compounds are disturbed, broken apart, or forced to react violently, "free radicals" are present during the period of disturbance. These fragments of the molecule are electrically neutral and are elusive, combining immediately with themselves and with other fragments of the broken molecule. In this picture, low temperatures of minus 200° C. have frozen these free radicals and are preventing them from reacting with the stable species also present in the bottle. Thus they can be studied and evaluated for use in new chemistry or new products and processes.

ticles, some of them truly strange as well as fleetingly transient. New types of accelerators will reach out into the 100 billion electron-volt region before 1970. What they allow man to discover may bring us new matter-energy relationships and new sources of energy more important than fission of uranium by neutrons.

For the present, coal, oil, and gas are the prime energy sources of our civilization, with uranium becoming useful to supply power where fossil fuels are scarce or remote. The great powerhouse of the solar system is our star-sun. Can the chemist duplicate the living plant's photosynthesis? Or can we go the green leaf one better by devising a synthetic food and energy factory using sunshine, water, and air as raw input?

For the energy to leave the earth by rocket (whether bound on missions of destruction or space exploration), chemistry is providing fuels that are far beyond the gunpowder of Fourth of July rockets or even the liquids of the V-2 rocket of World War II.

The nation's rocket engine industry has reduced to standard practice the use of nitric acid and aniline, of oxygen and alcohol, and of oxygen and gasoline. Next to be tapped are the high theoretical energy values of ammonia, hydrazine, and hydrogen as liquid fuels in combination with fluorine, and of hydrogen in combination with liquid oxygen or ozone. Solid rocket fuels, easier to store and handle, make savings possible by eliminating much auxiliary equipment and many services. Solid propellants include plastics, natural and synthetic rubber compounds, nitroglycerine, permanganates, and nitrocellulose compounds, as well as solidified boron compounds.

Brave new fields of chemistry are opened by new discoveries, concepts, and applications. Consider, for example, the research on the so-called *free radicals* which means more to the future than to the present.

Free radicals are a chemical form with potential importance for rocket fuels and other chemical products. Free radicals are molecular fragments that exist momentarily unless they are frozen at very low temperatures. They are the most concentrated form of chemical energy yet discovered. Ability to freeze them allows scientists to study them. Free radicals in the atmosphere are being considered as the power source for a solar rocket that would circle the earth indefinitely some sixty to sixty-five miles above the surface. Flames, paint drying, rubber synthesis, and a host of other reactions depend to some extent upon these building blocks which are normally short-lived. They seem to form a molecular bridge between the extremely speedy chemical steps that impart power to plant and animal life.

New materials and combinations have become available for higher temperature use and more resistant service. Cermets (ceramics and metals joined) and special alloys were developed for service at high temperatures. Titanium and various alloys were used more and more to resist corrosion. Other unusual metals were also snatched from their stubborn ores for exacting structural use. Even glass was successfully given strength, hardness and heat resistance hitherto limited to metals.

One of the most fascinating areas of industrial application of chemistry has been in the field of polymers. The plastics which are playing an increasing role in everyday life are polymers. They are made when long chains of molecules are fashioned from short ones. This technique called polymerization is basic to many kinds of chemical processes under the general heading of plastics. Shortly after the middle of this century, polymers represented

Hooker Chemical Corporation's new phenol plant at South Shore, Ky. Highly automated plant is being operated by Hooker's Durez Plastics Division and went "on stream" in late September 1962.

HOOKER CHEMICAL CORPORATION

Leo H. Baekeland.
Pioneer in
plastics development.

one-third of the volume of American chemical industry in dollars, 30.2 per cent in 1955 sales. To complete the picture, the other organics represented 53.0 per cent and the inorganics only 16.8 per cent.

The chemical beginnings of plastics go back to the time Leo H. Baekeland created a new class of materials by making the carbolic acid-formaldehyde synthetic which became known as bakelite. Continuing to be of major importance, the phenol-formaldehyde resins were joined by an array of other polymers. Some of the new polymers, such as nylon (polyamide) and dacron (polyester), supplied wonderful new textile fibers. Others, such as polyethylene, found a multiplicity of uses in everything from light-weight durable pipe to amazingly tough and convenient structural shapes.

Methyl methacrylate is a sort of organic glass, transparent and shatter-resistant. The beginnings of the plastic industry are significant, but only a start has evidently been made. Plastics run the whole range of properties from soft to hard, resistant to all

Wallace Hume Carothers.
Inventor of Nylon.

sorts of conditions, and capable of doing almost any job for which they are chemically fashioned. The synthetics are teaming up with natural plastics, the rubbers, and fibers. Irradiation of plastics gives rise to new, high-strength, flexible materials. Many discoveries of polymer chemistry are still in the future.

Chemical advance also made possible an amazing era of medical conquests with the help of sulfa drugs and antibiotics. This phase of the Chemical Era is in its way as startling and as important as the Atomic Era.

Relaxing drugs and tranquilizers joined the older chemical, aspirin, as a daily habit of many millions. New drugs, such as cortisone, let the lame dance and the halt hop. Even sick minds received their chemical treatments, ushering in new hope for the mentally ill who occupy more hospital beds than those physically ill. Will cancer succumb to chemistry in the not too distant future? Some forms of this dread disease have responded to chemical treatments. Pharmacological research promises still more wonders in the future.

To the farm, as to the hospital and clinic, chemistry brings added values. Gibberellic acid is a powerful new chemical that causes some plants to grow three times normal size and others to blossom in a week. It is a running-mate of growth promoters and weed killers. Even the tranquilizers promise usefulness on the farm, where they can quiet unruly livestock.

DDT and similar chemicals synthesized in the laboratories gave promise that man could overcome the very real danger of losing the battle for world supremacy to the insects. Epidemics of louse-borne typhus fever were prevented during World War II

Effect of Gibberellic acid.

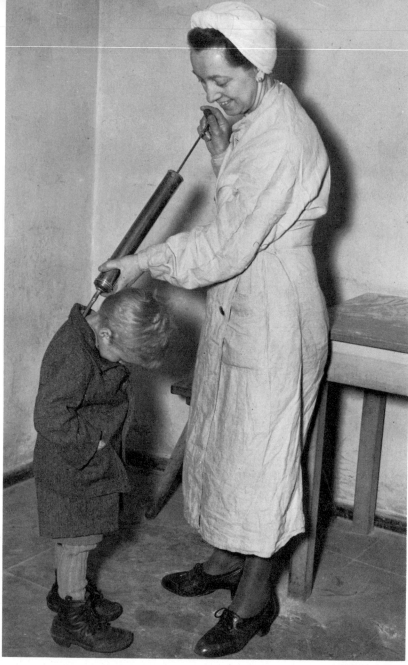

DDT, proved by extensive entomological tests to be toxic to a large number of insects including the body louse, and by pharmacological tests to be non-injurious to human beings when applied to their skin, protects our fighting forces against the typhus-carrying cootie. A refugee child at the Fricht Strasse Bunker, a German camp set up in Berlin for refugees, is having his clothing louseproofed without undressing.

by use of the newly produced DDT. To the time-honored insecticides of the previous century, there were added new chemicals that supplemented them and in some cases replaced them because of their greater effectiveness.

Chemical research became big business and profitable business during the century. The chemical industry grosses fifty billion dollars annually. Every large industrial concern found it fruitful to have research laboratories in which highly trained scientists

Beltsville research on insecticides.

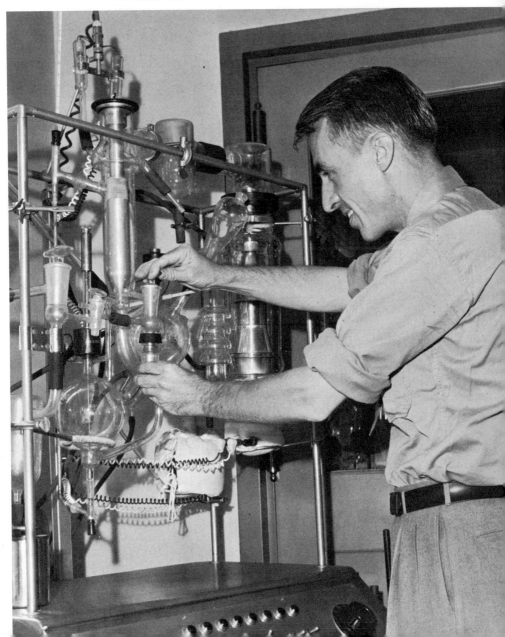

Du Pont's Sabine River Works at Orange, Texas, makes methanol, and intermediate chemicals for nylon and "Alathon" polyethylene resin.

of all sorts, not just chemists, could engage in group applications of science to their industry.

This technique of research in many respects was quite as important a discovery as the manipulations of elements and chemicals which were the subject of their researches.

THE
SCHEME OF
THINGS

THE DISCOVERIES and conclusions of science have had a tremendous material impact upon our civilization. Machines have been built, new methods and substances fashioned, and a virtual revolution created in daily life. From atomic discoveries have come both bombs and power.

The philosophical impact of new ideas and discoveries of science in the long run may be more far-reaching and revolutionary than the material effects.

At the turn of the century, from the standpoint of the ordinary so-called "common sense" physics of the day, our view of the way in which matter, time, and space interact was rather neatly stabilized, with not many questions asked and everything rather securely in place and apparently understood. There was no suggestion in the textbooks of the era that Newtonian mechanics would not be predominant for all time or that it might be unable, in the coming decades, to explain all the physical phenomena that would be discovered.

Unimaginative and unquestioning religionists and philosophers may have been upset by and antagonistic to the idea of evolution and, perhaps, the disturbing beginnings of the psychological attitude toward life. But they were unaware of the even more disturbing physical theory that was to be developed in the coming years. Those who saw and marveled at what seemed to be a logi-

141

cal and physical explanation for all phenomena were inclined to espouse a mechanistic view of life, as contrasted with an animistic or supernatural explanation of ultimate causes. Though self-satisfied in their knowledge, they were to have rude awakenings.

A pace of change, totally unprecedented in the world's history, began with the introduction of the quantum idea by Max Planck in Germany. From the study of the radiations emitted by hot solid bodies, Planck was forced to assume that light energy is not emitted and absorbed continuously by atoms; that is, that radiation including visible light is not a wave motion, as had been believed throughout most of the nineteenth century. Instead, Planck came to the conclusion that energy was emitted and absorbed in definite little bundles of energy, or *quanta*.

He worked out a peculiar universal constant, known as the Planck constant, h, where $h = 6.625 \times 10^{-27}$ erg-seconds, a figure that involves nearly all of physics, chemistry, and a good deal of astrophysics as well. Quantum ideas were not speedily adopted. They required much searching into the philosophical foundations of physics, a necessary step before they were to lead to more extensive predictions and formulations. Some of the consequences have had an impact upon the everyday thinking of many of those who cannot understand the physical implications.

Albert Einstein, who had not yet developed his theories of relativity, used the quantum theory to show how the photo-electric effect (emission of electrons from a metal when light shines on it) can be understood on the basis of the quantum view of light. This was the beginning of the dilemma of modern physics, the wave-particle duality.

Einstein's theories of relativity rose out of the conviction that inertial mass, as measured by Galileo, and gravitational mass, as measured by Newton, are not merely accidental. Classical physics explained many natural phenomena in terms of simple forces acting along straight lines by assuming a mechanical "ether." This idea was successful and predominant in astronomy. But the Michelson-Morley experiment on the velocity of light did not show a drift when light was transmitted in different directions. This destroyed the assumption of the existence of an "ether." Einstein determined that the planet Mercury did not behave according to the predictions of Newtonian astronomy, and that electromagnetic phenomena could not be wholly explained in

Professor Dr. Max Planck

terms of simple forces. As a result, he produced his special theory of relativity.

Einstein's general theory of relativity later enunciated the idea that energy and mass are interchangeable in the form of light. According to this idea, energy must have weight and must be deflected by a strong gravitational field. Confirmation of this theory came during the total eclipse of the sun in 1919, when light from a star was deflected as it passed by the sun. That demonstration gave relativity its currency, not only in the world of physics, but in everyday life. The theory also explained the inaccuracies in the orbit of Mercury around the sun, and accounted for the phenomena of electromagnetism. Less prominence was given to another consequence of Einstein's ideas in the early days of the century. That idea was that elements could be transmuted into other elements and that energy and matter

**Albert
Einstein**

are equivalent. This proved to be fundamental to the whole
atomic era.

Another physical and philosophical consequence of the Einstein formulation is the idea that absolute rest of an object is
impossible and that there is no such thing as absolute time. Absolute motion cannot be determined by any experiment and, in
the act of measuring, the participation of the observer affects
what is being measured. Another speculation is the possibility
that the universe is finite and yet unbounded. These were all
ideas alien and philosophically unacceptable to those who had
been raised on the classical or Galilean-Newtonian physics. Yet
they came to be accepted as the best explanation of what happens in the universe.

Such consequences of relativity have given rise to speculations
as strange as science fiction. This is the possibility that a person
sent speedily traveling into space will return much younger than

an earth-bound twin, a speculation which is intriguing if not very practical.

The first three decades of the century saw an exciting and ever swifter development of atomic and quantum theory on an international scale. Niels Bohr, in Copenhagen, in 1913 built his successful theory of the hydrogen atom. Max Von Laue, in Germany, showed that the regular arrangement of atoms in crystals would deflect X-rays in the same way that rulings of a diffraction grating diffract light. This provided a powerful tool for the study of solid matter. There was a succession of discoveries and theories that showed the duality of waves and particles. Werner Heisenberg, in Germany, discovered the mathematical way of treating problems of atomic physics that was called matrix mechanics. Then Erwin Schroedinger, also in Germany, formulated wave mechanics which was demonstrated to be the same as Heisenberg's theory expressed differently from a mathematical standpoint. Many others over the years made their contributions to the development of the field of physics. To list them all in a brief description is not possible.

Out of the ideas of quantum and atomic theory there arose the question whether it is possible to predict with certainty what will happen in a given situation. Is there an underlying fully deterministic description of the phenomena of atomic physics or is there some inherent limitation in the world which restricts human knowledge of events to conclusions of a statistical nature?

Heisenberg and Max Born in 1927 and 1928 came to the conclusion that, on an atomic scale, the processes of observation necessarily introduce uncontrolled disturbances. An increase in precision of knowledge had to be bought at the cost of uncertainty in some other variable. Thus, the determinism which we imagine and cherish remains an ideal toward which we can strive regarding large-scale phenomena, provided that limitations at the quantum level can be considered unimportant corrections. This has very real philosophical implications in everyday life, although the phenomena with which we deal generally are so gross that, within so-called practical limits, we can predict what will happen if we do certain things.

Not everyone is happy with this principle of uncertainty or indeterminateness. Not even the physicists themselves believe that it is necessarily true for the future. Einstein is said to have asked the question: "Would God play dice with the universe?" indicating that he felt the mathematical implications to be such that, some day, scientists would know with certainty a particle's path between two places separated by a determinate time.

It is probably unfair to apply these conclusions from modern physics to everyday life, and to use them for new contentions on the old question of free will or determinism. From the statistical indeterminism of quantum mechanics, the physicists will not support those who argue for the idea of free will in human behavior.

One of the consequences of work on structure of space and time was P. A. M. Dirac's work, carried out in 1928, which showed that all particles in nature must exist in pairs. There is an anti-particle for every particle of precisely the same mass and spin, but with an opposite charge. This suggests the existence of anti-matter somewhere in the universe. It is an intriguing idea that whole universes may exist with their composition so opposite to our own part of the cosmos that, should our kind of matter come together with this kind of anti-matter, there would be the most tremendous explosion conceivable.

The Dirac idea extends to the rather logical suggestion that, since in a mirror a right hand reflects as a left hand, there should be space reflection of the same sort. It had been accepted that there was no inner difference between right and left, a principle of parity that is philosophically appealing and was long considered true. In 1957, however, C. N. Yang and T. D. Lee, Chinese physicists working in America, showed that, for what are called very weak interactions between subatomic particles, this mirror experiment does not hold true. Their experiments showed that right-polarized neutrinos exist, but left-polarized neutrinos do not; that is, on reflecting a neutrino in a mirror, one would see nothing. This, too, is as upsetting to ordinary thought as the idea of uncertainty. Strong reactions which characterize many of the atomic actions seem "to behave themselves," but not the so-called weaker ones among subatomic particles. Most of the particles were discovered since World War II by observing the effects of bombarding matter with cosmic rays and man-made radiation from powerful accelerators. These particles show the weak interactions that are extremely important because they are responsible for the spontaneous decay of many particles. They do not behave as one would expect logically.

Thus, there are many unexplained facets of the nature of matter that must be explained in the further researches of physicists, who are confident that there will be increased understanding and perhaps a greater demonstration of the consistency and harmony in nature.

In recent years the number of so-called elementary particles has increased with rapidity, until there are now some thirty of them. In addition to the electron, the proton, and the neutron, together with their electrically opposite counterparts or anti-particles, we have nine other groups. Three are weightless light quanta, the neutrinos, and the anti-neutrinos. There are three more groups with a mass several times that of the electron. These are called mesons. The hyperons, another trilogy, are heavier than protons. The mesons and hyperons have extremely short lives, less than one-millionth of a second.

Great atom smashers are joining the natural cosmic rays, created in galactic super-accelerators of outer space. As the result of these atom smashings, scientists find the subatomic particles and study their interactions. Descended from the early cyclotrons and other accelerators that did so much to usher in the atomic age, the most powerful accelerators today are the twenty-eight-billion-electron-volt machine at Geneva operated by CERN and the thirty-billion-electron-volt accelerator at the Brookhaven National Laboratory, Long Island, New York. From these powerful machines, and others to follow them, will undoubtedly come new experimental information from which scientists derive more intriguing theories.

Joining physics and chemistry in picturing the nature of the physical world, mathematics played an important role, sometimes previewing entities that were realized to be physical and, at other times, formulating ideas that cannot easily be given physical expression. Symbolic logic was given impetus by the work of Bertrand Russell and A. N. Whitehead in their ambitious *Principia Mathematica* at the end of the century's first decade. Mathematics has had less influence upon everyday life in its abstractions and its formulations than many of the most advanced areas of physics. The modern approach to mathematics is one of greater abstraction than in the past. The older systems, which seem to have had more correspondence to the real world, are simplified, analyzed, and studied for their own sake.

Like physics, mathematics has had its own "soul searching." One of these disturbing discoveries was made by Kurt Godel in 1931 when he enunciated his law of excludability. It stated in essence that, whenever there is a mathematical system in which cannot be included proofs of the system's consistency, then the system must be abandoned.

There has been progress in pure mathematics, in which the ideas are studied for their own sake, often in very simple form. In applied mathematics more attention is paid to physical, chemical, or biological applications, and more emphasis is put on making mathematical models that correspond to the real world. Although this is a more classic and traditional kind of mathematics, all of modern technology calls upon engineers and scientists to learn it and apply it to their needs. In recent years many of the ideas of older mathematics have become whole new fields, such as statistics, mathematical physics, and even newer fields not yet as well developed, such as operations research and things of this kind. Many mathematical applications have been made to engineering, and some very interesting pioneer work done in psychology, sociology, and biology.

Many of these fields of applied mathematics represent extensions of work that has been done, problems that have been thought about for hundreds of years. In statistics, for example, Carl Friedrich Gauss in the early 1800's had discovered some of the mathematical distributions that were needed in statistics, and had advanced some of the basic ideas. Of course, not all of them; many of the others have been developed later.

In applied mathematics there has taken place a very important process of cross-fertilization between science or engineering and mathematical theory. In genetics the idea of the combination of genes, determining the characteristics of an animal, stimulated work on complicated probability problems. The basic ideas were very old. Conceptions of the kind of probability that you think about when you toss a coin, for example, go back to Bernoulli who lived in the 1600's, about the time of Newton; but it was not until this century, when Mendel's laws of heredity were rediscovered and ideas were advanced of what genes are and how they combine, that this kind of mathematics became useful to biologists. Such applications stimulated biologists to look for further ways in which mathematics could be useful in their field. Thus, R. A. Fisher in the 1920's, following Karl Pearson's statistical theory development, decided some mathematical ideas would help to plan experiments. In this way, mathematical statistics received one of its large impulses for growth.

In many fields of science, mathematics is the natural language for the description of theory. What can be said quite simply in mathematics is often difficult to say in words, and the clarity, logic, and conciseness of mathematics have proved very useful in thinking about the world.

Physics and mathematics, hand in hand, give us views of the world in which we live, explaining past mysteries and giving some insights into what will be learned in the future.

ELECTRONICS—
MACHINES AND
AUTOMATION

THE FLEETING ELECTRONS of electric current in its many forms have become the controllers of machines and mechanisms, replacing and supplementing the gross movements of levers, wheels, and similar devices of early stages of the industrial revolution.

While the use of electricity for power and the crude control of machines began before the coming of electronics, it was a succession of twentieth century discoveries and inventions that gave rise to the radio, television, electric eyes, photomultiplier tubes, tape recording, world telephony, radar, automation for machines and other devices, digital computers or electric "brains," and dozens of other applications.

The work done by electronic devices has a major impact upon communication, entertainment, education, transportation, manufacturing, research, medicine, finance, business and accounting, protection, and operations in the community, office, and home. Electron, or vacuum, tubes and succeeding electronic devices detect effects beyond the magnitude of our five senses; they amplify the extremely small which may be out of our sensory range altogether. They allow man to range the universe tuning in on distant universes, and let him tap the electrical impulses of living cells that probably make them animate.

Thomas A. Edison, while perfecting the incandescent electric lamp in the 1880's, actually made the first electron tube. In an unsuccessful attempt to prevent blackening in his early lamps,

150

he sealed a metal plate inside the bulk near the filament. He found that, if the plate was connected to the positive side of a battery and the incandescent filament to the negative, a tiny current would flow through the space to the plate as long as the filament was lighted. Edison saw no use for this curious effect, but it was the first electron tube, even if he did dismiss it and forget about it. J. A. Fleming, a young British engineer, repeated this experiment, remembering it when Marconi's demonstration of trans-Atlantic wireless, or radio, transmission in 1901 created the need for more sensitive detectors. Making a practical version of the original experimental Edison tube, Fleming patented it in 1905 as the Fleming "valve" detector, the first electronic radio tube. (The British still refer to valves to designate what is called in America an electron, or vacuum, tube.) In America a young radio experimenter, Lee De Forest, inserted another wire in the bulb, and shaped it like a gridiron. The resulting audion tube, or triode, as it was later called, was a better detector than the Fleming valve; not only could it detect, but unexpectedly it amplified very weak signals. This addition of the grid founded the new art that was to become known later as electronics and grow to more than a billion dollar industry.

First perfected and used for amplifying long distance coast-to-coast telephone conversations in 1914 by American Telephone and Telegraph's Bell Laboratories, to which De Forest sold his invention, the triode tubes were produced in the following years by the many millions for radio and for a myriad other controls of electric current flow.

Marconi's wireless was made possible by interrupted spark discharges that could be detected at distant points and read as dots and dashes of code. Ship wireless operators, known as *Sparks*, dramatically stood by sinking vessels until SOS emergency calls brought rescue on the high seas. Cables were supplemented by wireless between continents to supply the service that Marconi strove to establish. Vacuum tubes superseded the early wireless apparatus as signal producers. When wireless became radio, electronics began to come of age.

Radio broadcasting was the first great industry to arise out of the new electronics based on the vacuum tube.

Young amateurs experimented with both radio transmission and reception. They used the wonderful tubes which in receivers

Lee De Forest (*left*), inventor of the audion or triode essential to electronics. C. Francis Jenkins (*right*), who developed a system of mechanical television.

served both to detect and amplify. Their transmitters generated signals that carried talk. It was inevitable that song and music were soon in the ether for all to pick up. And in those days almost everyone could make his own radio in his own home. Simple receivers, without batteries, using natural crystals for detectors, were built by thousands out of parts sold in 5- and 10-cent stores. Newspapers told their readers how to build their own radio crystal-set receivers.

Broadcasting stations, commercially operated, began to supply music and news to these crystal-set enthusiasts. The government control and allocation of the radio frequency spectrum parcelled out wavelengths so that there would not be too much interference. The commercial manufacturers began to produce radio receiving sets, utilizing vacuum tubes capable of speaking loud enough so that all in a room might hear, instead of confining the listening audience to those with earphones clamped to both ears. At first, batteries were necessary to power the receiving sets which were not adapted to handle the high voltage and alternating current of commercial electrical supply. This disadvantage was overcome and batteries made obsolete by development of the receivers permitting radio sets to be energized by ordinary house current, in many cases without distinction whether direct or alternating.

The local broadcasting station began to be linked to similar stations in other parts of the country, at first over telegraph and telephone circuits which were not well adapted to transmission without distortion. But the technology of radio followed the demand as the telephone company provided nationwide networks of high-quality characteristics. Progress in long-distance telephony, made possible fundamentally by repeater stations using the same vacuum tubes that were basic to radio, served the geographically expanding radio broadcasting. The first transcontinental telephone line went into operation in 1914. When radio broadcasting became nationwide through the creation of chains of radio stations, telephonic links between the various parts of the United States were more nearly ready because of their expansion to meet the needs of private telephone conversation.

The impact and the possibilities of radio in national life were dramatized by the transmission and broadcasting of the inauguration of President Warren G. Harding in 1921.

In the beginning radio broadcasting was amplitude-modulated (AM), as most of the broadcasting stations are still today. But

Major Edwin H. Armstrong, inventor of FM (frequency modulation) radio.

the conventional AM broadcasting has noisy static, and the fidelity and quality of reproduction is not as great as desired. Frequency-modulation broadcasting, or FM, as it is called, was first demonstrated by Major Edwin H. Armstrong in 1935. It became an additional kind of radio being used by a relatively large number of broadcasting stations in the very-high-frequency band of the electromagnetic spectrum. In the conventional AM radio receiver, the variations in the size of the electrical oscillations that come to it determine the movements of a paper cone in the loudspeaker and, therefore, control the sound. The AM receiver cannot differentiate between radio signals and the intense electrical disturbances called static, caused by atmospheric conditions and thunderstorms. With FM radio, however, audio-signals are conveyed by varying the frequency of the transmitter in step with the voltage from the audio-signal and, therefore, do not pick up the effect of static.

FM broadcasting, despite its high quality and relatively low cost of building and operating a station, did not displace the AM broadcasting service, but rather provided a parallel system for the use of those who liked high-quality transmission and are willing to have the special kind of radio receiver required.

If television had not taken over electronic communication after World War II, FM broadcasting might have provided an increasing industry and service.

Television was developed in the laboratories in the 1930's, the principal patents being obtained by Vladimir Zworykin and Philo Farnsworth. Commercial TV began only five months before Pearl Harbor, at which time military needs took over both the manufacturing facilities and continued development.

Television, using an electronic scanner, reads across the scene as if it were a printed page, line by line, from top to bottom. It "sees" the optical image thus viewed and converts it to an electrical signal which is sent over a channel in much the same way that sound impulses converted to electricity are transmitted by radio or telephone. At the receiver, the video-signal is sent into an electron gun which repaints the viewed image upon a fluorescent screen. Both viewing and receiving mechanisms trace out the whole picture thirty times a second so that, using a principle similar to that of the motion picture, the eye is fooled into believing that there is movement.

Dr. V. K. Zworykin demonstrated the first electronic television receiver using the kinescope, or picture tube, which he developed together with the famed iconoscope, "eye" of the camera, in 1929.

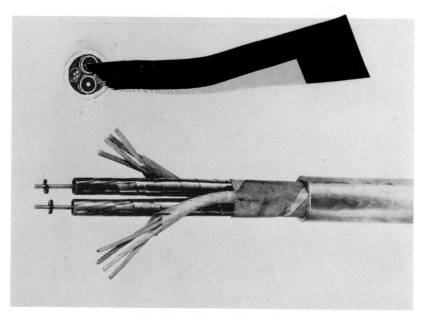

Coaxial cable used for TV.

Most of the millions of television sets in use are black-and-white, but color television became commercially available, receiving sets costing about three to five times as much as the black-and-white. Color sets separate images into three component colors for transmission which are recombined in the receiver.

Special channels for the transmission of television signals across the country are either coxial cables, which are special kinds of electron channels, or radio relays, in which beams are sent from tower to tower so spaced as to remain in a line of sight. Such facilities were needed for the distribution of television programs, and networks of them soon covered the country.

Television and the movies are competitors for audience time, with television winning out in many cases because it enters the home and there is no admission charge. Movies and television work together since sound films can be shown on television, and old releases provide programs to keep the television stations going during day and night periods when "live" or specially recorded programs are not available.

The sound motion pictures, which arrived when radio was young, were born of the union of phonograph records and silent movies. Later the recording and reproduction of sound on film, both by variable density and variable area, made the talkies more faithful and more self-contained. In these improved versions of sound motion pictures, electronics played a major part. An improvement or a new technique used in one application often brought beneficial changes in others. The same techniques that made possible more faithful recording of sound for the motion pictures provided better phonograph records, both for use on home recorders and for radio programs that could be produced at will and transmitted by the broadcasting station at a later appointed time.

A moving needle cutting into a disc recorded sound on a phonograph disc. This is still an important method of capturing and dispensing music of high fidelity. By putting two channels on the same record, it is possible to record and reproduce stereophonically, or to produce sound in depth. Magnetic recording from wire or, more prevalently, upon tape which contains magnetizable iron oxide, is a later version of recording electrical variations, useful in capturing and recreating at will sound and pictures alike.

Many thousands of miles of magnetic tape are used and reused every day in the broadcasting industry, and magnetic tape has also become a competitor of LP records for home music.

Recording upon tape has now supplemented and, in many cases, replaced the kinescope (motion picture) method of prerecording television programs. In 1953 television tape became operational and practical. About the same time successful methods of showing sound motion pictures in a combination of color and three-dimensional depth became commercial, giving the motion picture industry an edge over television. Color had come to the movies commercially between the two wars, the first technicolor feature appearing in 1935.

The rise of television and the entry into the home of often two or three sets per family did not render radio obsolete. The number of radio sets continued to be large, even though the rate of increase was not as great as for television.

The most important electronic development of World War II was radar, a word contracted from "Radio Detection and Ranging." It is a method of using special electronic equipment of very-high-frequency radio waves to detect and locate distant objects by means of radio echoes. During the war, hundreds of different kinds of radar sets were developed for use by the armed forces of, not only the United States and England, but Germany

Radar, BMEWS at Thule, Greenland.

and Japan as well. Radar arose from observations of echoes of radio waves which bounced back to us from the ionized layers high above the earth. From this interesting scientific observation came the device which was a prime warning and defense against attacking aircraft. The radio impulse of the radar set can penetrate the darkness, smoke, rain, and clouds, and can bounce back to show where an enemy plane or surface vessel is located. During the war, radar became the electronic eyes and the control of anti-aircraft guns. It detected attacking planes so that defensive planes could repulse them. Vessels guided by radar maps of their surroundings were able to cruise at full speed in the dark of night. Bombing planes carried not only an electronic mechanism to allow them to "see" the ground, but another to detect and determine the distance of attacking planes.

A radar transmitter produces short powerful bursts of radiation, about a millionth of a second in duration, that are repeated several hundred or several thousand times a second. The radio signal bounced back from the object being detected has its time of transmission accurately clocked, even though the echo travels at 186,000 miles per second, the speed of electromagnetic waves including light as well as radio. This travel time of the echo allows the automatic determination of the distance of the reflecting object.

After the war, radar became a splendid mechanism for guiding aircraft in flight. It is used to detect thunderstorms and other weather conditions ahead of airplanes. Also, the ground control approach (GCA), used to guide pilots into safe landing through clouds and fog, makes use of radar on the ground to measure the exact location of the plane over the field as it comes in for a landing. The operator on the ground, looking at his radar screen, talks to the pilot and tells him how to maneuver for a safe landing. More automatic and advanced radars are used in control and dispatching of planes, particularly at airports. Just as the radar contributed to success in war, it now helps commercial aviation.

Radar is still on watch throughout the world as a precautionary measure during the cold war. One of the most extensive installations stretches across arctic Canada, where the DEW line provides early warning of airplanes or missiles that may be carrying atomic bombs toward the United States. Even satellites carry

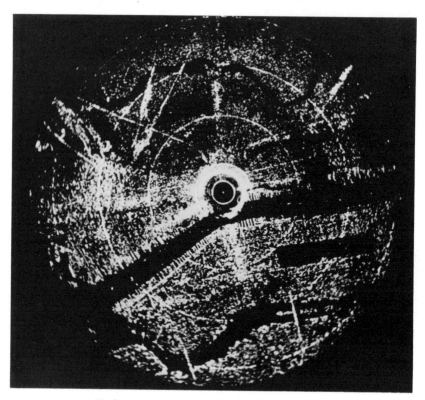

Radar scope photograph of New York City.

what amounts to radar. At various places throughout the world there are advanced mechanisms on guard, continuously collecting information on what is happening in remote parts of the world. Two decades after radar began to go to war, developments in radar had advanced so far that hope was held out that commercial airliners (or enemy bombers) might be watched as they fly across the Atlantic. This form of radar is able to see beyond the horizon by bouncing its electronic beams off the ionosphere. Such devices also would be able to detect what is happening at distant points, without actually being in foreign countries themselves or flying over them.

Many new methods have been devised under the impetus of making electronic apparatus lighter, more effective, and more reliable, so that the devices may be put into missiles and space vehicles, taking up little room and with the least expenditure of pay load possible.

One of the secret devices of World War II was the proximity

fuse which was used decisively in the closing days of the war. This is an electronic device which explodes an artillery shell at a predetermined distance from the ground or its target. It is essentially an adaptation of radar. The proximity fuse wiring of the conventional sort used in radio sets was too cumbersome and, for that reason, the electrical circuits were printed in metallic ink upon insulating material. These printed wire circuits found use in industry. As a result, radio sets and hearing aids were miniaturized when the printed wire circuit was combined with the new amplifying device known as a transistor.

Arising out of research upon the chemical elements (germanium and silicon) that are called semiconductors and evolving out of studies of what is called the solid state, a new kind of detecting and amplifying electronic device was developed. This is known as the junction transistor. Transistors can do the same job as vacuum tubes, but they have the great advantage of being more sensitive, more stable, and not needing to be warmed up before they go into action. Transistors were not invented until 1948, and they did not get into effective production until about 1953. Battery-operated radios of small size were possible because of transistors' sensitivity and the small amount of current needed to operate them. Radio sets became almost as portable and convenient as small cameras. Radio had escaped from bondage to commercial electric current supply, using batteries no more complex than those for flashlights. Applied to television, transistors promise to make possible battery-operated television sets.

Following upon the development and the utilizations of the transistor came other devices that, at the beginning of the 1960's, have held out promise for useful development. Many of these are made, like transistors, from relatively unused and strange metals and metallic compounds. Among these are germanium, silicon, gallium, and other materials which are known as "semiconductors," so-called because they conduct electricity better than insulators but not as well as metals. These semiconductors need small amounts of impurities in the metals to make them work. The principle of the transistor uses electrons; that is, electric current is made to flow from the "n" or negative side of the junction in the semiconductor material to the "p" or positive side. This flow occurs when an external or regulating voltage is applied. To assure sufficient conductivity, traces of other elements, such as boron, aluminum, gallium, and indium are introduced to provide free electrons or negative charges, and phosphorus, arsenic, and antimony to give an excess of positive charges, called *holes*. "P"-"n" junctions are the key to action in other new electronic devices.

The maser, a word standing for "microwave amplification by stimulated emission of radiation," consists of solid crystals which are caused to oscillate at microwave frequencies. They are made of gadolinium ethyl sulfate diluted with lanthanium ethyl sulfate in the chill environment near absolute zero. Their utilization promises to effect improvements in several fields of electronics.

Another device that works best at low temperatures is the cryotron, so-named because of the cryogenic ranges in which it operates. In its simplest form, the cryotron consists of a straight

A present-day transistor unit with its component parts is held in the palm of the hand while the award-winning miniature transistor, developed by Diamond Ordnance Fuze Laboratories through the utilization of photo-lithographic processes and printing techniques, rests on the tip of the index finger.

piece of wire about one-tenth of an inch long, wound with a wire about the size of human hair. It operates in a bath of liquid helium. At such low temperatures its metal offers little resistance to passage of electrical currents. The operation of the cryotron depends upon the central wire being made superconducting. Then, by raising or lowering the magnetic field in the surrounding coil, the conduction in the central wire is changed, and the device makes or breaks connections in an electrical circuit. In this way the cryotron can control larger currents.

Another new technique is called molecular electronics, which makes possible building a complete communication receiver the size of a pea. Semiconductor crystals in the form of long thin ribbons are incorporated in such devices without any intermediate material processing. Each crystal is a complete electronic device. Molecular amplifiers have the potential of former devices a thousand times their size and may, therefore, be adapted for use in missiles and satellites.

During World War II, in connection with radar, crystal diodes served as frequency converters, eliminating vacuum tubes previously used for that purpose. Noise generated by those vacuum tubes had masked incoming radar signals and limited the sensitivity of the equipment. The diode was a semiconductor silicon unit sealed in an especially designed case, millions of which were produced during the war years.

Another kind of diode called the tunnel diode, also made of semiconductor materials such as germanium, silicon, and later the compound, gallium arsenide, causes an interesting effect called "negative" resistance because the resistance becomes smaller with an increase of voltage impressed upon it. These diodes were important because they work like a switch. This is particularly useful in computers. Switching rapidly from a high resistance to a low resistance can be done using a small voltage. A tunnel diode does not have a visible tunnel, but it depends upon the fact that across the "p"-"n" junctions there is a way for electrons approaching a potential barrier to cross it. According to a principle in quantum mechanics, there is a small but finite probability of an electron disappearing and instantly reappearing on the far side of the barrier.

Other methods not strictly electronic were developed to do some of the operations for which electronic circuits were utilized.

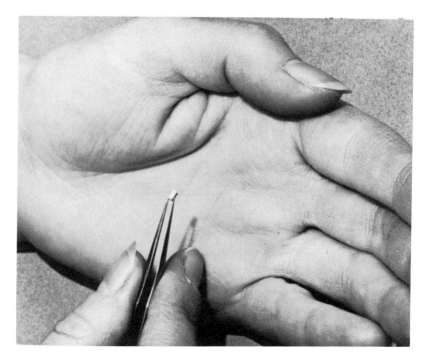

Tunnel diode—The tiny device in the man's hand is a tunnel diode, the youngest wonder among electronic devices. General Electric Company's gallium arsenide tunnel diode works at frequencies above 4,000 megacycles.

Some control equipment used liquids or gases instead of electricity, and had no moving parts. Fluids, either liquids or gases, operated through passageways in blocks of metal or plastic, with one stream of fluid working against another stream and controlling it.

In another development, tiny droplets of liquid are coated with a thin layer of gelatin to become capsules, each a millionth of an inch in diameter. Besides other applications, they can make up an assemblage of tiny electric cells which can become a memory device. Tiny capsules containing light-sensitive dyes are activated by one kind of light, read by photoelectric cells, and erased by another kind of light.

Electronic methods make possible prodigious and useful memories that can store extraordinary amounts of information with great speed. These memory systems are utilized to perform an amazing variety of functions. In a computer, various devices such as magnetic tape are used to hold data and supply them upon mechanical demand. In the case of the latest telephone systems, microscopic memory spots on photographic plates can create a program of action when orders are given the system by telephone dialing. The electronic memory can be temporary. For instance, in the most advanced telephone switching mechanism there is a semipermanent memory, employing barrier grid tubes, that records the status of calls and lines, a sort of "scratch-pad" memory. The capacity of these machines to remember is fantastically large and the speed with which they work extraordinarily fast. They work in microseconds; this electronic speed may be emphasized by the fact that there are more microseconds in a minute than there are minutes in a century.

Their speed of operation was a great asset of the computers that came into existence after World War II. In some cases, although problems could be solved by computation, it was not feasible to do so in pre-computer days because it took too long to make the mathematical computations. With computers many complex problems necessary for practical solutions could be presented to the machines and solved in sufficient time to be of practical use. A machine can do in an hour or so what would require a lifetime of work by a skilled mathematician. Moreover, when the machine is given instructions for a solution, it is very faithful in carrying them out with great accuracy. Orders can even be built into the instructions to select an alternative procedure according to the results of the previous operations. It was a next step for the machines to perform repetitive logical thought processes instead of merely numerical calculations. Thus, the machines take over tedious brain work, relieving human intellects of some of these tasks.

During World War II, a two-hundred-ton electronically coupled differential analyzer worked on military problems at the Massachusetts Institute of Technology. The first big computer was the ENIAC (a name contracted from electronic numerical integrater and computer), built at the University of Pennsylvania. It contains eighteen thousand vacuum tubes. This machine, invented by J. W. Mauchly and J. P. Eckert, was the forerunner of a whole family of electronic computing devices which now have been produced by a dozen or more organizations and applied to a wide variety of tasks, including design computation, control of machines, keeping of banking and payroll records, storing and producing information upon demand, and translating one language into another, although this proved to be a very difficult problem which had not been solved satisfactorily at the beginning of the 1960's.

Machines that can feed written information into computers, without the necessity of human operators punching it on tape or cards by operating a keyboard, progressed to an experimental stage. These print scanners operate by looking at printed characters, recognizing them, and converting them into a code that the computer can accept and store.

Little wonder that with machines doing these things and many

World's first automated ice cream plant, in operation at H. P. Hood and Sons in Boston, makes treasured treat of young and old alike with aid of pushbuttons and a computer. The Minneapolis-Honeywell installation is completely automatic from blending of ingredients, called the mix, to freezing tanks. Computer "thinks out" recipe, then codes formula on a punch card. Coded recipe card is read by other electronic devices which open valves and measure flow of ingredients to blending tanks. Pasteurization, homogenization and cooling processes are remotely controlled from a programming console. Automatic operation even includes in-place cleaning of lines and tanks after ice cream is made.

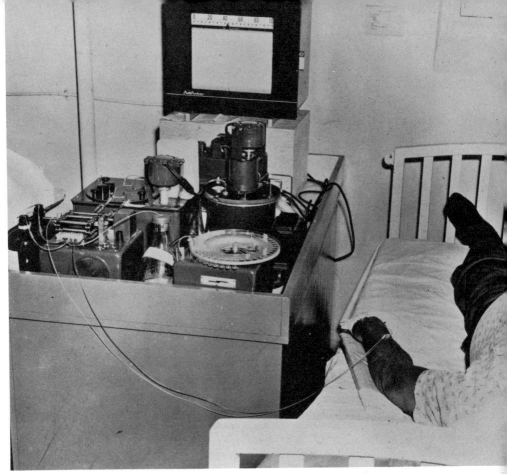

Clinical investigation by Auto Analyzer.

more they are called *thinking machines*, and admired for their "brains," as well as their brawn.

Automation began in the early days of the century before electronics, although its early development was well within the vacuum tube period. Before the First World War, fully automatic turret lathes permitted one operator to tend several machines. High-speed carbon steel for cutting tools advanced the industrial age. The "assembly line" was an invention that accelerated the mass production of goods. Henry Ford proved that it was practical to bring parts of machines to the workers instead of having workers take the parts to an assembly site. So effective was the application of mechanization to factory production that the inanimate parts of the process soon proved to be more dependable than the human operators who, from a mechanical standpoint, were often unreliable. In automation the endeavor was to replace human fallibility with mechanical reliability and perfection. The

The **IBM STRETCH** computer, one of the world's most powerful, is now in use at the Weather Bureau's General Circulation Research Laboratory, Washington, D.C. The computer will be used by Weather Bureau meteorologists to simulate global weather in the laboratory for new studies of how and why our atmosphere behaves as it does.

machine was made to imitate and apply one of the methods by which human beings have advanced; that is, seeing that they have made errors and then correcting them. The machines become inspectors as well as workers. The idea of the feed-back was applied to electronic circuits. The use of control units that regulate themselves, depending upon what automatic electronic inspectors report, is essential in automation.

Automation, with electronic controls, can be applied in almost every factory or processing operation. Metal parts are guided through hundreds of operations without human intervention. Electronically guided machine tools are capable of doing delicate cutting, drilling, and welding operations. Automatic controls measure and adjust temperature, pressure, quality, and speed of flow of oil and chemical processes.

Electronics is suggested as a traffic safety aid. The use of electronic devices could make highways automatic. Impulses along the roads could guide and control automobiles and prevent collisions. This possibility in the not too distant future has been shown by experimental vehicles.

Not content with the mere control of machines and mechanisms, some scientists turn their thoughts to the possibility of thought itself being translated directly into recording and controlling devices without rising to the level of realization or perhaps even consciousness. The behavior of man and his thought processes consist of electrical impulses in his brain. Can these innermost human attributes be tapped and fed into machines? Such is the daring dream, perhaps not suggested in full seriousness. Nevertheless, nerve impulses are being explored, using the most advanced electronic apparatus.

There is recognition that the human mechanism and brain, often storing detailed memory of a whole lifetime and synthesizing many varied experiences, is still the master computer in comparison with the most advanced electronic device. It is a consequence of advanced scientific thinking and aspiring that man can think such thoughts and ponder on such potential progress.

Here, Dr. F. W. Reichelderfer (*right*), Chief of the Weather Bureau, and Dr. Joseph Smagorinsky, Chief of the General Circulation Research Laboratory in Washington, D.C., examine elevation contour map of the Northern Hemisphere as printed out by the STRETCH computer. Topographic contours are used as part of the input data needed to simulate weather processes with the laboratory's new computer, one of the world's most powerful. The STRETCH console and magnetic tape units can be seen in the background.

U.S. DEPARTMENT OF COMMERCE

SEX, GENETICS, AND LIFE

FROM THE EARLIEST DAYS of life upon the earth, even before the rise of mankind, it was evident that like begets like. The stream of life was continuous, whether through the dividing of the amoeba or the joining of male and female in higher animals and plants. Thus, the basic facts of the continuity and maintenance of life were implicit in instincts that preceded rational animals and the blossoming of reason and science. The full significance and the science of it has been discovered in recent years.

It has been only within this century that the facts of heredity and genetics have been understood, appreciated, and utilized. The Austrian monk, Gregor Johann Mendel, reported the historic conclusions from his experiments in 1865, but no one paid attention to them. Not until 1900 did Hugo de Vries in Holland, Karl Correns in Germany, and E. Tschermak in Austria rediscover Mendel's findings and thereby initiate a new science. This ranks in importance with the fissioning of uranium or Darwin's work on the *Origin of Species*.

Mendel crossed a round-seeded and a wrinkle-seeded pea plant and found that all their offspring were round. He then crossed the offspring among one another; their progeny were part round and part wrinkled, in the ratio of three round to one wrinkled. The contributions of the two parents did not merge into a new hereditary trait, but were recoverable unchanged in later generations. He observed that the yellowness of the round peas and

170

Gregor Johann Mendel (1822-1884), Austrian Augustinian monk who discovered the first laws of heredity.

the green of the wrinkled peas was not necessarily transmitted so that a specific color was always linked to a particular form. Thus, there arose the concept that the hereditary makeup is an assembly of independent units—a concept that is fundamental in the architecture of heredity.

The hereditary elements were found to be in the small, but microscopically visible, bodies of the cell's nucleus, the chromosomes. From experiments with fruitflies, sweetpeas, and other fast-reproducing organisms, it was demonstrated that the hereditary units, called genes, occupy specific places in the chromosomes.

Herman J. Muller

Most of the genes are stable and are passed on from generation to generation without change, preserving the character of living organisms with remarkable fidelity over generations.

Genes can change to bring about forward or backward steps in heredity. Most of them are backward, that is, bad rather than good for the animal or plant. When genes change, they undergo what is called mutation.

Mutation seems to be the mechanism of evolution. Perhaps it was cosmic rays which, pounding the earth from outer space over the long eons of time, caused mutations, thereby producing the gradual differentiations that allowed the multiplicity of plants and animals to arise on our planet.

Man can take steps to change the genes and produce artificial mutations. H. J. Muller in 1926 proved this using X-rays and related radiations. Later, it was found that some chemicals can produce such effects in genes—for example, mustard gases and carcinogens.

Atomic-bomb explosions of the fission kind throw radioactive materials into the atmosphere, contaminating the earth and its life, and bombarding the genetic heritage to produce harmful mutations. The atomic sins of today are visited upon our great-grandchildren.

One reason that there is no great public alarm over the damage radiation can do is that radioactivity from atom bombs, in the form of fallout, or X-rays, such as those used in the doctor's office or for chest X-rays, does not hurt or sting a person, not even as much as sunburn. It is an unfelt menace.

All the authorities agree that increased radiation from any source will be bad. Some differ over how bad the effect of radiation is on human beings of this generation. The United Nations report of 1958 suggests that the margin of uncertainty is so great that low doses of radiation may produce no somatic effect, at one extreme, or that, if low doses do produce leukemia, the prolonged continuation of atomic testing may cause five thousand to sixty thousand cases a year. This is a prospect of atomic peace.

The greatest danger is not so much to individuals now alive, but to millions who will be born in the next thousand years, perhaps even the next generation.

The National Academy of Sciences report on the biological effects of radiation estimates that, if the whole population of the United States received a small dose of extra radiation—even as small as one roentgen—among the next hundred million children to be born, several thousand would be definitely handicapped because of radiation-caused gene mutations. True, many more would be handicapped from spontaneous mutations that would have happened anyway, but, no matter how hidden, those radiation-damaged children would be a result of the extra radiation from bomb testing or atomic war explosions.

That one roentgen increase is only 10 per cent of the ten roentgen amount that recommendations say should not be exceeded from birth to age thirty.

Genetically, there is simply no end to the radiation damage visited upon the children, grandchildren, and the ever-so-great-grandchildren. Only a small fraction of the damage will be in the first generation, although it will be noticeable then. Half the damage would occur in thirty to fifty generations, which is a long, long time, since thirty generations is about a thousand years.

Radiation-induced mutational effects, detected as malformations, still-births, various diseases, and increased death rates, are mimicked by various other causes, including spontaneous mutations.

More fearful is what would happen to the genetic future of mankind if the U.S. and the U.S.S.R. began to throw atomic bombs at each other. Some visualize, in addition to the millions upon millions killed in the initial blasts, such effects upon human heredity that humanity would never recover.

Mutation changes can only be harmful to man's heredity. We cannot experiment genetically with human beings. Even if we could, there is neither enough control over people, nor enough time, to pursue the genetical attempts at change that are being used in plants and even other animals.

Other such experiments have been tried.

The classic use of X-ray-induced mutation was by Milislav Demerec to increase the yield of penicillin from the Penicillum strains, well submerged in the immense culture vats in which this antibiotic producing organism grows. High doses of X-rays caused mutations that produced a new strain, which increased previous yields more than four-fold. This became the basis for the enormous production of penicillin that has contributed so much to national health.

From many millions of irradiated seed, there may arise one or two seedlings that could produce new and better varieties. But the real successes of genetics have come from selection and hybridization, using the laws of heredity that stem from Mendel.

Hybrid corn is the prime example of the great achievement of genetics in increasing the food supply, and preventing it from being outdistanced by world population—a fate that Malthus so darkly predicted. In the early 1900's, E. M. East, then at the Connecticut Agricultural Experiment Station, and George Harrison Shull, of the Carnegie Institution, independently had the idea for a new method of corn breeding. With a few others who made this theoretical achievement a practical possibility, they brought about a two-thirds increase in the United States yield-per-acre of the corn crop. This was achieved without increase in the labor needed; in fact, because of its uniformity, hybrid corn is easier and cheaper to harvest. Literally billions of dollars have been added to the income of the nation.

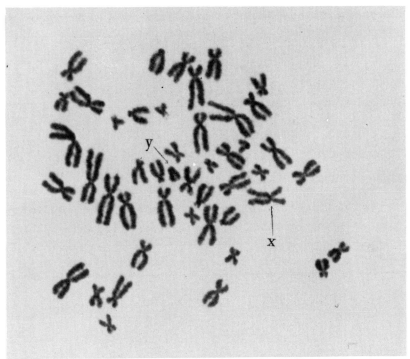

The somatic chromosomes of a human male.

The increased yield of hybrid corn produced during the war years, 1942–1944, was valued at two billion dollars, as much as the cost of developing the atomic bomb. Even more important, this increase in the corn crop was greater than the food that the United States was able to ship to the desolated countries of Europe just after the war.

Inbreeding of the plants was the first step. Corn has both sexes on the same stalk, the tassel being male and the female flower being lower down, tufted with silk. In inbreeding, individual stalks are isolated, bags are placed over the tassels, and collected pollen is sprinkled over the female flowers of the same plants. This inbreeding produced strains that showed a marked loss of both vigor and productiveness. They were very pure strains of great uniformity, although totally worthless to the farmer. When, however, two inbred lines were crossed together, there was a phenomenal improvement. The hybrid ears were large and full, equal to or better than the best strains of the time.

But a "double cross" was needed to produce the present-day

hybrid corn planted on some sixty million acres. Invented by Donald F. Jones, double cross in corn breeding had quite the opposite connotation from the usual meaning of the term. By crossing together two hybrids from the single crosses of four different inbred lines, seed was obtained for crops that exceeded in vigor and yield even the hybrids of the first crosses. This is the way hybrid corn seed is produced.

Similar genetical procedures have been applied to many food plants and animals.

Life begins in minute spheres of jelly-like protoplasm, about the size of the point of a pin, which develop into intricately organized living aggregations of billions of molecules. If these protoplasmic globs are human, they result in beings that can grow, adapt, think, remember, and communicate—who can create and appreciate art, literature, religion, science, technology, and all other cultural wonders of civilization. They can hand down to the next generation the biological and cultural inheritance evolved through the ages, and they can do this generation after generation.

The human organism is the most intricate form of life, but every kind of animal and plant shares fundamentally in the wonderful mechanisms of heredity, a fortunate fact of Darwinian evolution that has allowed experimentation and the discovery of some of the fundamental aspects of biology in the decades since Mendel.

Inside the egg cell, which is the start of a new life, are the chromosomes, twenty-three each from the mother and father. These carry the genes that contain the directions for building a person, determining male or female, brown or blue eyes, tall or short, the color of hair, disposition to disease, and thousands of other characteristics. There may be as many as 10,000 to 100,000 kinds of genes in the nucleus of the human egg, each controlling some factor in an individual.

The principles of Mendelian inheritance have been investigated in mice, protozoa, corn, algae, fungi, bacteria, and particularly in the very simple viruses. So simple chemically are some of the viruses that they are made up of only two classes of molecules, contrasted with the many thousands that are involved in man. Working with such relative simplicity, scientists found that the T2 virus, favored for genetic investigations, is made up of proteins and deoxyribonucleic acids, abbreviated DNA. By studying how the virus particle infects a bacterial host cell, watching the process through electron microscope photographs, and tracing radioactively labeled atoms in the molecules, scientists determined that the primary genetic material of a virus particle is DNA. Through experiments with more complex life, DNA was shown to be the key genetic material.

DNA seems to be the fundamental stuff of life at the molecular level.

In the molecular model of DNA, proposed in 1953 by two Cambridge University scientists, J. D. Watson and F. H. C. Crick, there seems to be a structure to account for four essential properties of genes: information content or specificity, precise duplication or replication, mutation, and function. The complexities—or rather the simplicities, when one considers the immense detail of the genetic process—involve another form of nucleic acid, called ribonucleic acid, or RNA, which serves along with

Stuff of life—The wad of DNA, or deoxyribonucleic acid (*left*), is the substance that holds the pattern of life. The model on the right shows the DNA double helix, or coil, with the four nitrogen bases.

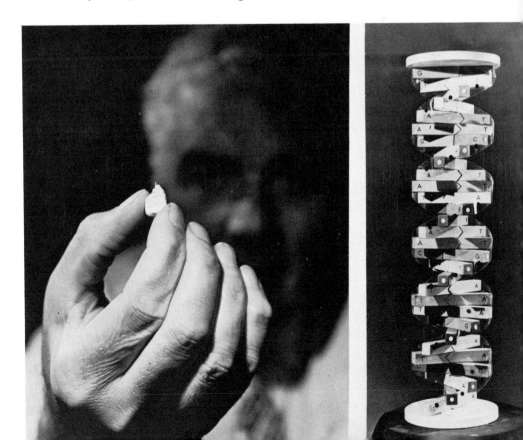

DNA model scale.

DNA as a sort of template in building the proliferating structure of molecules.

Thanks to this new knowledge of gene structure, life can be defined as ability to replicate in the manner of DNA, and to evolve through mutation and natural selection. This is a great step forward in dissipating the classic mysteries of life and man's desire to set it apart from the rest of the universe.

Biochemists may be expected to produce, in test tubes, molecules that "live." They should be able to reproduce the conditions of the beginnings of life on earth a few billion years ago, and to demonstrate that life arises when conditions are favorable. This is the logical consequence of our genetical progress.

Application of this new genetical knowledge to the conduct of human affairs and the flow of human generations, so much a matter of emotions and propinquity, is for the future when more is discovered and meshed into the stream of human consciousness.

FOOD
AND
AGRICULTURE

As a result of the application of science to agriculture, the production of food in America is so effective that the worry of the mid-twentieth century is surpluses and not shortages. The population, as a whole, is not threatened with hunger but with the danger of eating too much. Reduction of weight has become a fetish as well as a health measure.

America's surfeit of food is an exception in a starving world. In great areas upon the earth there is real hunger and a continuing lack of enough food, both in calories and the right kind of nutritive value.

While America has embarrassing food surpluses, in which over eight billion dollars is invested and one billion dollars is needed annually for storage and preservation, they are a consequence and a tribute to scientific agriculture, and to the remarkable progress made through research practice and operation, largely during this century.

When the nation was young, at about the time that the Constitution was adopted, nine out of every ten working persons were employed on farms, and farming was at a near-subsistence level. By 1900 such progress had been made that only 38 per cent of the persons gainfully employed were engaged in agriculture. Twenty years later the percentage dropped to 27 per cent, at mid-century it was 11 per cent, and in the sixth decade it was reduced to as low as 9 per cent. One farmer was growing food and

179

George H. Shull

vegetable fiber for twenty-two persons besides himself by 1960, a far advance beyond the pioneer struggle for existence when the population spent most of its efforts feeding itself. The farm population was actually approximately two-thirds of what it had been at the beginning of the century.

The prodigious food production with less human labor has banished the fear of famine in the country. It has released many millions of the population to become industrial producers and city dwellers. The greater efficiency in agricultural practice is due to a combination of factors among which, most importantly, are mechanization resulting from the internal combustion engine, the production of more efficient crops and animals, and the control of plant and animal diseases.

In the preceding century, large farms had utilized steam-powered tractors, but the horse was still the dominant form of power on the farm. Gasoline farm tractors developed parallel with the automobile and, by mid-century, tractors outnumbered the horses on American farms. Much of the hard manual labor of farming was transferred from human backs to machines.

Small tractors took over from horses, and electric power lines spread through rural America to give the farmer and his wife conveniences equivalent to those available to city dwellers.

The great crop for human bread, wheat, was made more productive through introduction of new varieties from other parts of the world, breeding to bring about disease resistance, and development of superior varieties. Corn, due to scientific development and the introduction of hybrid varieties, increased magnificently in yields of bushels per acre, compensating for damage caused by the invasion of the corn borer.

Cattle, both for beef and milk, were improved through scientific breeding. Hens were developed to increase egg production remarkably, and chickens for meat were so improved that they could be sent to market earlier, having produced more meat for less feed.

Chemical insecticides, imported diseases, and parasites were pitted against insect pests. New chemicals were discovered that speed the growth of plants or control unwanted weeds in the fields. Rigorous barriers to the importation of dangerous and unwanted insects and plants were established to protect American agriculture.

For the journey of farm products from fields to human mouths, science and technology provided new methods and processes. To the cans of food, which were the first big step in making the food supply independent of the season, was added food frozen near the farm, and kept fresh and ready for consumption weeks and months later by freezers in stores, restaurants, and homes. Mechanical refrigeration displaced ice as a means of preserving so-called fresh food above the freezing temperature. The calendar no longer dominated the menu.

The importance of food factors which, in very small quantities, affect health and prevent disease increased the appreciation of certain kinds of foods. Once the effect of the vitamins had been discovered to prevent various nutritional diseases, chemists isolated these factors chemically and in many cases synthesized them so that they could be made from non-food sources. Natural foods were, therefore, supplemented or enriched during processing. Animals that provide human food also benefited from the knowledge of vitamins and the discovery of other elements essential to their diet. The soil nourishing the plants was found to need added amounts of various chemicals in order properly to support the crops grown. Trace elements became important in fertilizers.

There was realization that additions to food can be harmful as well as beneficial. Dr. Harvey W. Wiley with his "poison squad" of human volunteers dramatized the desirability of safe food preservation and the dangers of harmful chemicals, such as benzoate of soda. The pure food law resulted, and government control over the purity of food as well as drugs was established. Federal inspection of meat was also instituted, as a means of preventing transmission to human beings of animal diseases, particularly tuberculosis.

The revolution in corn production that scientific development of hybrid seed corn made possible is the most significant advance

Hybrid corn.

Henry A. Wallace, Secretary of Agriculture, about 1933.

in food production of the century, perhaps of the whole history of agriculture. Corn, or maize to use its international name, is probably the most important food crop of the world. It is not seen on American dinner tables as widely as wheat and other crops, because the greater part of the gigantic corn crop goes into feeding livestock or supplying industry. Corn reaches our kitchens and dinner plates as beef, pork, lamb, poultry, eggs, butter, milk, and cheese. It appears in our homes in hundreds of industrial products. To us today it is nearly as important as it was in the early days when the Indians taught the first settlers at Jamestown and Plymouth how to plant, grow, and harvest this life-saving crop. In this century, the most significant development of research in crop production has been hybrid corn, which gives a yield of about two-thirds more per acre than had been possible previously. Hybrid corn was a major factor in increasing farm output with a dwindling farm labor force.

The way in which hybrid seed corn is produced is quite different from the way in which farmers traditionally grew their crops, carefully selecting seed from the previous year's crop.* The investment in seed corn must be made anew each year because hybrid corn gives its unusual yield for only one year. But corn farmers found that the extra cost of the seed was well worth the money.

In the early trials of this new idea, double-crossed strains

* See pages 174–76 for description of hybrid-corn production.

New hybrid wheat. The American-Japanese hybrid semi-dwarf wheat has been named Gaines in honor of the cerealist who bred the first smut-resistant wheat for the Pacific Northwest. Dr. O. A. Vogel, an agronomist for the U.S.D.A. at Washington State University, is its breeder, and has bred several other varieties of winter wheat for growth in the Pacific Northwest.

yielded one hundred to two hundred bushels per acre on the same soil where standard Connecticut varieties were yielding eighty to ninety and the inbred parents less than forty bushels.

Many of the experimental stations and a considerable number of scientists continued to explore this discovery. Finally in the mid-twenties, largely through the efforts of Henry A. Wallace, who was later Secretary of Agriculture, Secretary of Commerce, and Vice President of the United States, hybrid seed corn became available to farmers. It introduced a virtual revolution in corn growing which added many millions of bushels of corn to crops throughout the world. As Wallace said when he first reported the possibilities, it affected directly or indirectly every man, woman, and child in the corn belt; it changed our system of farm management, and even affected the domestic policies and the foreign relations of the United States.

In the breeding of grain, such as wheat, oats, barley, and rice, there has been a continual improvement in yield, quality, and disease- and insect-resistance. New varieties are introduced into the country from abroad, selections made of the best varieties, and hybridization conducted through methods that have been very carefully and expertly developed, largely by the U.S. Department of Agriculture and state agricultural experiment stations, but also in part by private breeders. Constant changes have been made in leading wheat varieties, largely to counter the inroads of disease and the damage by insects. Types of wheat that were satisfactory in the past often do not continue to be grown because newly introduced varieties mature earlier, protected from insects, rusts, and fungi.

Over four hundred commercial varieties of wheat have been grown, but a score of them, distributed among five classes—hard red winter, soft red winter, hard red spring, white winter, and durum wheat—are responsible for most of the acreage in recent years. Most of the kinds of wheat grown are of relatively late vintage, but they have the heredity of grains introduced in previous decades, sturdy qualities which are theirs through selection or hybridization. Improved varieties of wheat are distributed to farmers at the rate of about three to five per year. The result has been greater adaptation to regional conditions and increased resistance to rust, smut, other diseases, drought, winter killing, and insects. Sometimes a new variety takes over relatively fast because of superior qualities. Marquis and Ceres had dominated the wheat fields, but were hard hit by stem rust. Then came Thatcher, which was resistant to stem rust, but other varieties more resistant to leaf rust, bunt, and mildew appeared in their turn. The triumph of scientific plant breeding is that varieties of wheat can be made resistant to insects as well as disease. The Pawnee variety of hard winter wheat, for instance, is particularly resistant to Hessian fly.

In the case of other field crops, there has been continual improvement of varieties and a scientific fight against disease by breeding new kinds of these crops.

Were it not for scientific agriculture and plant introduction, as well as breeding of new varieties, such great crops as sugar cane, cotton, rice, sugar beets, and various kinds of forage would be much less profitable and productive. In some cases it might have proved impossible to continue to raise a crop if science had not played its part. Mosaic disease and curly top at one time threatened to wipe out the important industry of sugar beets and sugar cane. Other crops were created by scientific improvement. Improved varieties of soybean developed by research brought this crop to major importance.

The war against insects in agriculture, as in other phases of life, has never ceased. While there have been some setbacks and permanent conquests by the insects, mankind has been able to survive the invasions. In one case, the arrival in the United States of the serious citrus pest, the Mediterranean fruit fly, which gained much ground in Florida in 1958, was resisted and this insect eliminated by a strenuous and arduous eradication campaign. Both the corn borer and Japanese beetle, which arrived at about the time of the First World War, are with us still and promise to be permanent residents.

Sex plays an important part in the clever methods used by entomologists in their fight against insect pests. In one instance, male flies were bred, sterilized by X-rays, and released so that, when they mated with females of the species, another generation did not result. By a similar method, a chemical that sterilizes both male and female houseflies and fruit flies was mixed with their food. The chemical produced by the female gypsy moth to attract the male of the species has been synthesized to be used in detection and possible control of this insect pest.

The synthetic organic compound, DDT, made its first major contribution to the control of insects, such as the body louse spreading the human disease, typhus fever. But it also proved to be a major aid to farmers and gardeners in their unending campaign against pests that plague their crops. Since its introduction during World War II, DDT has been widely used. It almost wiped out pests of many kinds: flies that bothered cows and people alike, vermin in house and factory, bugs big and little in garden and field. There were difficulties, however. DDT sometimes got into the milk of treated cows and thereby into human bodies; it also killed beneficial insects and birds. Some of the in-

Sexual trickery—Chemical that sterilizes insects is spread in a dump on a small, uninhabited Florida island in tests which proved the success of desexing male houseflies and reducing the population of pests.

U.S.D.A. PHOTO

sects, such as tough houseflies, survived and developed resistant strains to defy DDT attacks. Some insects had then to be fought with other insecticide materials, such as pyrethrin and rotenone, either derived from plants or made synthetically. New types of organic fungicides were produced that were more effective in specific fields than the old ones made of copper and sulfur compounds. To fight rats and other rodents, chemical warfare with new compounds was used.

Because chemicals used to fight the insects and the fungi are in some cases harmful to humans who consume the treated food and vegetables, chemicals inimical to the crop predators but of low toxicity to humans have been sought and developed. Insecticidal residues are limited by law. The new organic chemicals are not as overtly poisonous as arsenic, lead, and their compounds that were more widely used before the arrival of the DDT era. There must be a continual search for new compounds. It takes about five years to test and safely introduce a new organic insecticide even after it is synthesized and demonstrated to be useful.

Paralleling what DDT and other compounds have done in the control of insects, 2,4-D and related chemical compounds have come into use for killing and checking the growth of weeds. A weed is a plant that the farmer does not want in his field. 2,4-D is particularly effective against such plants as dandelion and wild mustard, that hitherto have had to be hoed out of the fields. Solutions of 2,4-D sprayed on brush and brambles clear away this unwanted vegetation. Poison ivy is one of the plants that 2,4-D kills effectively. Old-fashioned hoeing or cultivating to prevent competition of weeds with crops has not been completely outmoded, but these new chemical compounds with specialized qualities are bringing helpful new control and cultivation techniques to farm and garden.

Another chemical, called gibberellic acid, causes plants to develop like Jack's fabled beanstalk. In some cases, this chemical accelerates plant growth to two or three times normal size. It can also cause early flowering, faster germination, and speedier seed development. It has even made it possible for plants like rye to produce grain without the natural cold treatment of winter weather which is called vernalization. Originally isolated from rice, gibberellic acid has given impetus to a search for

Newborn hairless pigs showing symptoms of iodine deficiency.

similar substances in the seeds and fruit of other plants with the
hope that they will have specialized useful effects.

The importance of the creation of new plants through scientific methods was recognized by the inauguration of a new class
of U.S. patents in 1930. The plant patent law provided that a
patent could be obtained by anyone "who has invented or discovered and asexually produced any distinct and new variety of
plant other than a tuber-propagated plant." The clause of the
law about "asexual" varieties was arranged to prevent a monopoly
on cereal grains, and the tuber-propagated exception was designed to prevent a monopoly on potatoes. The sometimes spectacular and highly publicized "plant wizard" work of Luther
Burbank, as well as the support of Thomas A. Edison, brought
about this addition to the patent laws. The first plant patent,
issued in 1931, was for a climbing rose "characterized by its ever
blooming habit."

Research to improve the production of livestock and poultry
to meet human needs and desires has been as successful as the
research development of better plants for American farms. In
cattle it was possible to breed the kinds of animals that produced
beef most efficiently and bore heavier calves that matured faster
on less feed. By careful selection, milk cows were developed that
are extraordinary converters of feed into milk from which dairy

products, including butter and cheese as well as milk, are obtained with a quality and economy never before possible. When the American dinner table commanded pork with less fat and more lean, new types of hogs were developed to supply the desired kind of hams and bacon. And they did it more economically.

Poultry production was revolutionized with improved strains of chickens, higher efficiency in the use of feed, and control of disease. Less food was needed to produce a broiler in a shorter time, with eight pounds of food for a three-pound broiler in ten weeks a routine production figure in the mid-1950's. As a result of rigorous selection and breeding, hens kept pace to raise the national average to 145 eggs per hen per year from about 60 less when the century was young.

Artificial breeding, particularly in cattle, greatly accelerated the production of superior animals and raised the level of dairy and meat production. Now superior bulls can sire great numbers of progeny through the use of artificial insemination, a technique that has been utilized in the U.S.S.R. since about twenty years

Cattle diseases—Veterinarian injecting tuberculin.

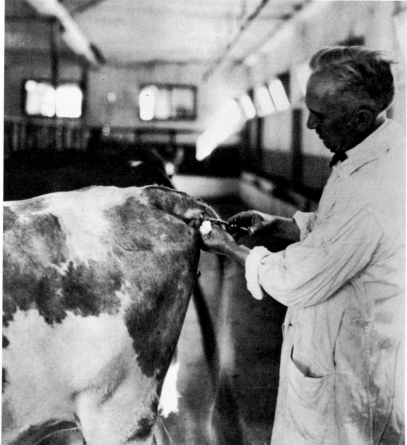

PHOTO BY WATSON DAVIS

Santa Gertrudis Cattle.

before it was started in America just before World War II. A bull can service thirty to fifty cows a year in the conventional way, while through artificial insemination two thousand cows a year may be impregnated from the same bull. Artificial insemination was utilized in the beginning to speed up the rate of livestock improvement, but it has become widely practiced for its convenience and saving in money.

The various breeds of cattle in the United States, usually raised with close attention to keeping the herds pure for each particular kind, were developed in the nineteenth century largely from imports. The outstanding new breed developed in this century is the Santa Gertrudis of the King Ranch in Texas. This breed resulted from crossing Brahman bulls from India with Shorthorned cows, producing a kind of cattle highly adaptable to the semitropical Gulf Coast. Similarly the Brangus breed was derived from the Aberdeen Angus and Brahman. The Beefmaster is a cross of Hereford, Shorthorns, and Brahman. Sheep of a new breed were derived in a like manner from the crossing of Rambouillet and Lincoln breeds. New kinds of hogs were developed by crossing Danish Landrace with Tamworth to obtain Minnesota No. 1, with Hampshire to obtain Montana No. 1, and with Poland China to obtain Beltsville No. 1.

The animals that furnish meat and other products for our

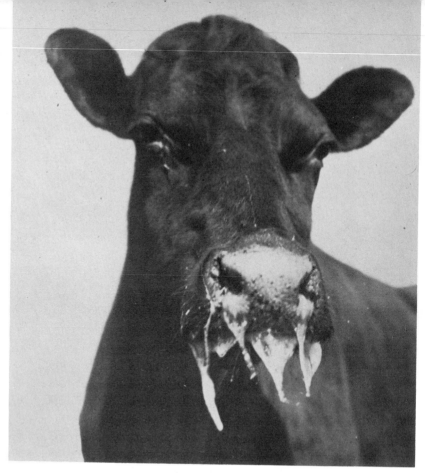

Cow with hoof and mouth disease.

dinner tables suffer from diseases which must be controlled or eliminated. Early in the century, hog cholera, a serious disease, was brought under control by the development of a serum produced in pigs that have acquired immunity. Injections of this serum prevented large economic loss from the disease. Methods have been worked out to prevent disastrous diseases in poultry, in part by cleanliness as well as immunization. Control of poultry disease, especially pullorum in chicks, was achieved by the detection and elimination of hens carrying the infection from flocks raised for hatching.

Tuberculosis is a disease in cattle that has been eliminated largely by repeated tests for the disease and removal of infected animals from the herds by slaughter. The foot-and-mouth disease, an extremely contagious infection in cloven-footed animals, was eliminated from the United States by rigorous quarantine and immediate slaughter of affected and exposed animals when it appeared in the country on a number of occasions within the century. During the war, there was great fear of biological warfare that might have introduced into the nation various diseases of animals, such as rinderpest. The development of a vaccine against this extremely serious disease alleviated the fear of its malicious or accidental introduction with disastrous results. Some previously serious animal ills are now kept under control. For instance, tick fever and its losses have been eliminated through the eradication of cattle ticks by systematically dipping the animals in troughs filled with arsenical solutions.

In the nineteenth century the gross characteristics of food and their various classes—carbohydrates, fats, and proteins—were recognized, and food value, as measured by energy content in calories, became known. It was not until the beginning of the twentieth century, however, that experiments largely on animals demonstrated that lack of certain dietary constituents could cause disease. The discovery of the vitamins, or accessory food factors, and a realization of their role in human nutrition took place as the century progressed. Unlike the bacteria and viruses that cause diseases through their presence, the lack of vitamins causes illness. Some of the deficiency diseases were recognized for long

USDA PHOTO

Eight-week-old chicks—Larger chick from egg injected with vitamin B-12, smaller chick from egg not treated.

Perosis, or slipped tendon—a disease of chickens marked by bone deformities and associated with high intake of inorganic phosphate or calcium salts and low intake of manganese.

USDA PHOTO

periods in the past and, in a few cases such as scurvy, were even prevented. A ration of limes on British ships prevented scurvy, an empirical finding. The scurvy-preventing vitamin, ascorbic acid or vitamin C, is one of those that a succession of scientists recognized, isolated, and used to maintain health.

The roll of the vitamins runs through part of the alphabet. The public knows of the existence of vitamins and their functions through advertisements that urge taking vitamin pills. The most essential vitamins most likely to be left out of the human diet have been added to foods, beginning in World War II days, so that almost everybody obtains an adequate supply. This enrichment of food began as a war measure, and has been continued with such success that vitamins are a part of the American diet. Almost everyone eats the foods—bread, milk, margarine, etc.—in which they are incorporated.

Diseases due to nutritional deficiencies were prevalent in the early decades of the century. In 1928, for example, there were more than seven thousand deaths attributed to pellagra alone, the niacin-deficiency disease, primarily seen among people who ate large quantities of corn. Niacin or nicotinic acid, as it is called, is one of the vitamins that were added to white flour and white bread. The other additions were thiamine, or vitamin B, which combats beriberi and heart disease; iron, a preventive of anemia, and riboflavin, necessary for normal eyes and skin.

Research work by scientists identified, isolated, and synthesized these essential vitamins so that they became available in sufficient quantities at low enough cost to make feasible their addition to common foods. Bread, the most widely consumed of all processed foods, eaten by people of all income brackets at most meals, was chosen to carry the vitamins required to prevent nutritional deficiencies. Vitamin D, a lack of which leads to rickets, retarding calcification of bones, is added to milk in some cases, while vitamin A, whose lack plays a role in night blindness, is added to some margarines.

Due to a suspected relationship between cholesterol and hardening of the arteries, or atherosclerosis, fats of vegetable origin, such as corn oil, came to be preferred to animal fats. This was a demonstration that medical theories or findings, when widely publicized, could affect food distribution and even the agricultural economy.

In the complexity and confusion of world politics and agriculture, the Food and Agriculture Organization of the United Nations was created after the war to coordinate and implement international action in improving agriculture, particularly in the less developed areas, and to distribute agricultural surpluses to

A yearling Belgian filly suffering from vitamin "A" deficiency.

U.S.D.A. PHOTO

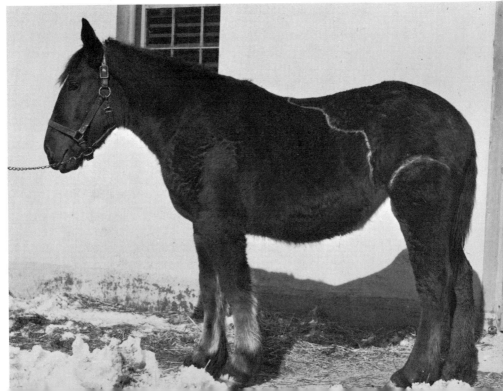

areas with food shortages. Sir John Boyd Orr (now Lord Orr), the first Director General of the FAO, analyzed the situation and proposed a world food board plan. This was not accepted and implemented, although it would probably have been a powerful aid in solving some of the tremendous social and economic problems of the world.

The discoveries and applications of science have given the world enough food to maintain an increased population in greater health and well-being. Hopefully, international and political relationships will allow the scientific gains to be maintained. Hunger should be banished eventually from the world if the dangers of war and international conflict can be avoided.

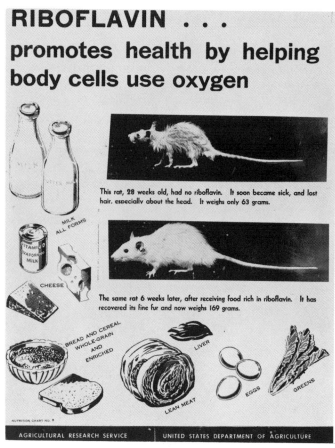

U.S.D.A. PHOTO

Nutrition charts.

FLORA
AND
FAUNA

Living things upon the earth have evolved through many millennia. Many of the animals and most of the plants are far older than man. A few decades of a century are an extremely short period for natural evolution to have any effect. Plants and animals change, not so much in their fundamental character as in their prevalence, range, and opportunity of impact—often dependent upon what man does to the environment, directly or indirectly.

The numerical increase in the human race, a virtual population explosion, is the predominant biological fact upon earth today, overshadowing in effect if not in numbers what has happened in recent decades to various kinds of plants and animals.

The census of species of living things has not changed in modern times. More than a million species of plants and animals had been named by the middle of the century, more than 625,000 of them insects. When the gigantic task of describing all the flora and fauna on earth has been accomplished, at least twice this number will assuredly be recognized. The estimates of the total living insect forms alone are set at from 2,000,000 to 4,000,000 by some entomologists. This is not the number of individual insects, but the kinds or species. Scientists will not attempt to estimate the prodigious numbers of individual insects in the world; the censuses attempted of just a few acres give gigantic figures, and the world figures would be nearly incomprehensible. The small

197

Thousands of ducks darken the skies with a rush of wings, spurred by a mysterious urge to head south in the fall.

size of many of the creatures, their rapid reproduction, and prolific multiplication with an adequate food supply skyrocket the numbers astronomically.

Microorganisms abound, both in kinds and numbers. They constitute a teeming world of their own, cleaning up the wastes of nature as well as causing diseases of man, other animals, and plants. Modifications of these living forms take place; some may even be disappearing from the face of the earth, but probably not in the short time period being considered.

The rise of new species has not occurred in recent decades and cannot be expected. Some of the changes brought about by man's manipulation of heredity may possibly be so radical that they will be judged new species, but this is doubtful. The conservative classifiers, who keep track of the kinds of living things through extensive national and international collections, in museums, will be slow to come to the conclusion that such differences are worthy of being called new in a species sense.

Among larger animals, such as mammals and birds, some species are known to have disappeared from the earth. Two of the best-known examples are the dodo and the passenger pigeon. Before the turn of the century other animals, once numerous, had also become extinct—among them the Merriam elk, Labrador duck, Carolina paroquet, sea mink, great auk, and heath hen. The ivory-billed woodpecker, the largest woodpecker in North America, has probably joined the ranks of the extinct because no authentic reports of its existence appear since 1952. The most publicized species threatened with extinction is the whooping crane, a magnificent bird nearly as tall as a man, with a wing spread of almost seven feet. When America was discovered, there may have been relatively few in existence, perhaps not more than

U.S. FISH AND WILDLIFE SERVICE

Whooping cranes have made a comeback due largely to public concern for their existence which led to the creation of the Arkansas National Wildlife Refuge in Texas on their hereditary wintering grounds.

1,400. But when a fight for the survival of this bird was made, including the preservation of its hereditary wintering grounds in Texas, the whooping cranes began to make a comeback. Only the future will tell whether the effort has been successful.

Other birds that may be doomed to extinction are the California condor, the Florida Everglade kite, and the nene, or Hawaiian goose. Some species and subspecies of birds are becoming endangered through land use trends, but others—including the trumpeter swan, the Hudsonian godwit, and the eastern turkey—are no longer considered in danger because they have been given protection and their environmental conditions have been changed.

On the list of candidates for extinction is the bird of the country's national emblem, the bald eagle, which once ranged over most of North America. The species has a total population of about one thousand, concentrated in Florida and Alaska, the extremes of its original homeland. Though protected by Federal law, "Old

Eastern heath hen—Despite frantic efforts of the state of Massachusetts, the last bird of the species died on Martha's Vineyard in 1931.

The bald eagle once could be found throughout most of North America. The population of the species is now estimated at about one thousand, and it is concentrated in Florida and Alaska, at the edges of its original habitat. "Old Baldy," the bird of our nation's national emblem, is now protected by federal law. However, it is a good target because of its size, and the young eagles are often shot, being mistaken for hawks.

Baldy's" size makes it an enticing target. Too often young eagles have been mistaken for hawks and shot.

A million Attwater's prairie chickens are thought to have ranged over the coastal prairies of Louisiana and Texas at one time. As a result of pollution from oil drilling, rice farming that destroys their grasslands, and drought, only a few thousand remain.

Other feathered species that must be considered on the endangered list are the Mississippi kite, swallow-tail kite, white-tailed kite, Florida sandhill crane, Laysan teal, Aleutian tern,

Trumpeter swan, a bird that was threatened with extinction, no longer is in danger, because of protection.

Florida burrowing owl, peregrine falcon, red-bellied hawk, Kirtland's warbler, and Cape Sable seaside sparrow. There are also the limpkin, flamingo, woodcock, reddish egret, American egret, snowy egret, roseate spoonbill, and great white heron, largest and rarest of the herons.

Bird species are not the only ones threatened with extinction. Many mammals, fish, and reptiles are also in danger. The best known of the menaced mammals, perhaps, is the grizzly bear. In 1960 there appeared to be fewer than eight hundred grizzlies still remaining in the United States, excluding Alaska, about one-fourth of them within the boundaries of our national parks. Other endangered mammals include the sea otter, tule elk, black-footed ferret, kit fox, manatee or sea cow, Key deer and Caribbean monk seal, Sierra bighorn sheep, desert mountain sheep, woodland caribou, gray wolf, red wolf, walrus, wolverine, and coyote.

In other parts of the world a fight is on to save the mountain gorilla in Africa, the Ceylon elephant, the giant tortoise and land iguana of the Galapagos Islands, the Bactrian camel of Asia, the pigmy hippopotamus in Africa, the cheetah of Africa and Asia, the Javan rhinoceros, and the markhor on the borders of Pakistan, Afghanistan, and the U.S.S.R.

Two North American reptiles are also in peril—the green turtle and the American crocodile. Among rapidly disappearing fish species are the lake sturgeon, grayling, Great Lakes whitefish, and lake trout.

Over one hundred forms of mammals alone are estimated to

Desert mountain sheep—This young ram was photographed in the Kofa Game Range, Yuma, Ariz., as he approached a water hole. He climbed the rock in order to locate the camera. Among the most surefooted of animals, these sheep are diminishing in numbers.

have become extinct in the last two thousand years, and at least seventy-three have disappeared since 1800.

Selective breeding in the Munich Zoo has duplicated types of animals that have simply been encyclopedia references for many years. Isolation from mixed stocks of the characteristics of originals re-created the aurochs, the ancestor of domestic cattle, and the tarpan, the European wild horse which became extinct a century ago. This is the reverse of the way in which nature or man created new breeds of animals out of existing stock.

At times there have been comebacks from extinction due to the discovery of specimens of supposedly vanished species. Most noteworthy was the dredging of the Coelacanth from the waters of the Indian Ocean off South Africa, demonstrating that this fish, supposedly extinct 70 million years ago, and known previously only from its fossil form, actually exists in the depths of

Grizzly bears—There appear to be fewer than eight hundred grizzlies still remaining in the United States (excluding Alaska), about one-fourth of which are found within the boundaries of our national parks.

Coelacanth—A fish which there was every reason to believe had died out completely before the end of the Mesozoic Epoch—probably fifty million years ago. The capture of this big coelacanth in South African waters constituted one of the most startling discoveries of a "living fossil" ever made. The fish is five feet in length; the photograph is taken from a cast at the South African Museum.

the ocean. The ancestry of the Coelacanth can be traced back 325,000,000 years to the group from which descended all the land vertebrates, of which man is a recent development. This makes it one of the oldest types of back-boned animals known.

The Puerto Rican whip-poor-will, supposedly vanished from the earth, was rediscovered in a Puerto Rican forest through the playing of tape recordings of its night songs.

The tuatara is known as the "midget dinosaur" because it is the sole survivor of the order Rhynchocephalia, which flourished 200,000,000 years ago. This reptile, believed to be extinct on the New Zealand mainland, was found to exist on the North Auckland peninsula.

Little snail-like creatures were dredged up from the depths of the Pacific Ocean and found to be the oldest living representatives of the primitive ancestors of snails and chitons and, possibly, the clam. This snail-like Neopilina had been thought to have been extinct for some 300,000,000 years, and is considered the earth's oldest kind of multi-celled animal.

Evidence for life on earth goes back to the beginning of the record of the rocks. Evidence of plants almost three billion years old has been discovered. And in rocks on the shore of Lake Superior ancient organisms, believed to be microscopic animals, have been determined to be two billion years old, or four times as old as those fossil imprints of the Cambrian geologic age.

Such antiquity of life on earth demonstrates the beginning of a long drama of evolution. The living record thus extends to the early epochs of the earth itself.

This continuance of life is built upon individual plants or animals, generation after generation. For bacteria and viruses each generation exists only a fleeting moment; for man it is seldom more than a hundred years, but for individual plants, such as ancient trees, it may extend for millennia. The oldest living thing on earth is the battered wreck of a pine tree with more than four thousand years under its bark, a living entity that was venerable when King Solomon ruled Israel. This is one of the bristle cone pines in California's Inyo National Forest, in the White Mountains east of San Francisco near the Nevada border. The bristle cones, many of them, are five hundred to a thousand years older than the Sequoias.

The scientific delvings into the evolutionary past of plants and animals, including man, are directed to the future as well as having the obvious purpose of finding how life arose and underwent modifications in the earth's past history. Nature's successes and failures in modifying various kinds of life, as proved by the fossil record, give hints and suggestions of how the stream of life can be manipulated to raise more desirable animals and plants. Natural modifications cannot be expected in the few future decades with which we are primarily concerned. Powerful new methods of modifying heredity through human intervention have developed, some of them more potent imitations of the ways in which natural forces move to achieve the changes evident today. For instance, mutations produced by the effect of radiation upon genes can result from planned experiments or the natural impact of cosmic rays, as well as atomic bombs. A possible beneficial by-product of the rising menace of atomic radiation spread through explosion of atomic bombs may be new plant varieties, even modification in animals, apart from the danger of induced cancer in animals and human beings.

When it is possible to manipulate the chemical constituents of the bearers of heredity within the genes, the chemicals DNA and RNA, as scientists confidently expect to do, the world will see new forms of life which may be sufficiently different to be considered at least new breeds and races. If this happens in the coming decade, it will be a culmination of the growing knowledge of evolution and genetics, which to a great degree has been a twentieth century achievement.

Breeding and hybridization have developed successful new kinds of animals and plants. Almost every kind of grain, vegetable, cattle, poultry, swine, and other economically important domesticated flora and fauna have felt the impact of the good breeders. There are hens that lay more eggs. There are new kinds of cattle with altered genes from the hybridizing of breeds that have desirable characteristics, such as the Santa Gertrudis cattle adapted to the climatic and range conditions of south Texas and other parts of the world. Such successful design, manipulation, and building of new qualities into plants and animals utilizing the stock and strains of previously existing kinds is one of the great achievements of the century.

Fear that the insects would inherit the earth was prevalent during the first few decades of the twentieth century, but the development of methods for fighting insects gives new assurance to man that he will not succumb to the insect menace, although he may be decimated by the potential atomic disaster that he has created.

Insects and microorganisms of an extraordinary variety and durability carry diseases to humans, animals, and plants. They ravage growing and stored crops. In the warmer parts of the earth, they make life uncomfortable, if not dangerous.

Poisons began to be used against insects and plant diseases before this century. The powdered element, sulfur, was used as an insecticide and fungicide centuries ago. Bordeau mixture fungicide made of copper sulfate, lime, Paris green (poisonous arsenic and copper), was an outstanding success in the nineteenth century. But a revolution and major offensive against insects began with the availability of such chemicals as DDT, the principal chlorinated hydrocarbon. The old and new pesticides are responsible for the flawless fruit and vegetables that come to our dinner table.

Not all the insects perish in man's chemical warfare. Some survive and their immunity to insecticides is passed on to the next

An especially equipped plane spraying insecticide against grasshoppers.

generation. New chemicals are devised to be used upon insects immune to the old insecticides. Some of these new weapons are organic phosphorus compounds, related to the nerve gases devised for military chemical warfare, but not used in human combat.

There is need for care in using insecticides to prevent them from contaminating the food they protect and thus endangering human health. Regulations were tightened to prevent harm to the public and to agriculturists as the dangers became apparent. The major illnesses and deaths from insecticides occur primarily among the people who apply them without proper precautions.

Parasites, predators, and disease organisms are used to control insects. Natural enemies of insects are imported to fight insects when they invade new territory. A classic example is the destruction of the cottony-cushion scale of citrus fruits in California by the Australian ladybird beetle.

Methods of biological control are constantly being sought. As mentioned, sexual trickery is being used as a means of reducing the insect population by making male insects sterile. The infertile males are released. The normal females lay eggs that do not hatch and thus the chain of life is interrupted. This has been done very successfully with the screwworm which attacks all breeds of livestock and has caused losses averaging twenty million dollars a year. Millions of male screwworm flies are sterilized with radiant energy from the atomic by-product, cobalt-60. The same plan is being used on other insects. Sterilization is being accomplished by means of chemicals as well as radiation. Houseflies, some of which become resistant to DDT and other insecticides, are candidates for effective control by male sterilization method.

It should be remembered that there are some insects beneficial to man that are unappreciated in our preoccupation with our enemies. The control methods must preserve the good insects.

Man himself is the most dangerous animal antagonist of man, from the time men fought in caves until now, when atomic forces threaten civilization. But the insects and disease microorganisms rank next in dangerous antagonism and competition. Only in the twentieth century has man seemed to come within reach of safe and eventual ascendancy over the rest of the animal kingdom.

Man, instead of being dominated and limited by the rest of the living world, has the prospect of using animals as a new and socially acceptable class of living slaves, competitive with machines.

The historic record of co-operation between men and animals is best exemplified by the now partially outdated symbiosis of horse and farmer in America, and the psychological companionship of dogs with people, principally children, lonely women, and outdoor-loving men.

Through experiments and studies of animals in psychological

laboratories, the possibility has arisen that what we can learn from animals may even be applied to our ways of doing things in our automated civilization. It may even be possible to utilize chimpanzees, pigeons, and other animals to do repetitive tasks in factories. Work by Professor B. F. Skinner, a Harvard University psychologist, and that of other investigators has demonstrated the possibility of training animals to do useful jobs by what is called operant conditioning or reinforcement theory. In the case of animals, they are deprived of food, then given small amounts as reinforcement for performing a specified task or group of tasks.

Many thousands of visitors to the U.S. Science Exhibit at the

Enos, a 5½-year-old chimpanzee, is fitted into his pressure couch prior to a three-orbital flight from Cape Canaveral, Fla.

NASA PHOTO

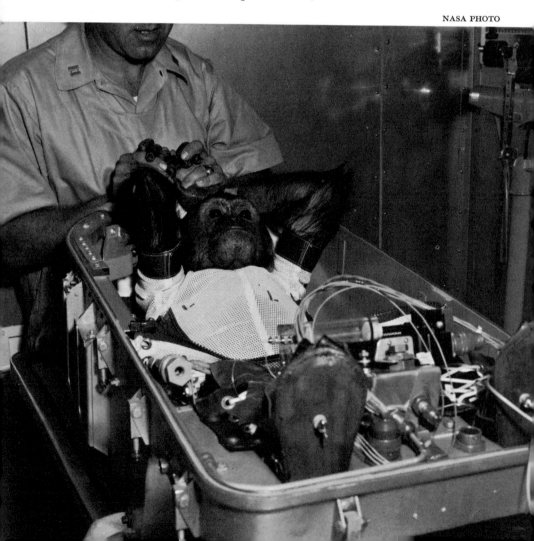

Seattle World's Fair saw pigeons industriously pecking the right key when certain signals appeared, then automatically rewarded with a small amount of food. One of the U.S. space shots, before human astronauts were put into orbit, used a monkey as a stand-in, and this animal performed tasks on order to demonstrate that it was withstanding the trip satisfactorily.

Such tests and demonstrations with animals have allowed the development of new methods that can be used to control human beings, although usually the reward for which the humans strive is not merely food. Whether chimpanzees could be trained economically to compete in the repetitive labor market (they live about two-thirds as long as a man) and actually be used in factories remains to be seen.

Animals have seemingly many abilities that are mysterious to scientists. How do the migratory birds find their way over long distances? How do the eels travel over long sea distances to spawning grounds? Why is the dolphin or porpoise, that makes speech-like sounds, able to communicate with its fellow animals and outsteer electronic devices to its objectives?

More experimentation with such animals will give explanations and possible applications in many fields. Man is intelligent enough to learn from other animals.

HEALTH
AND
MEDICINE

HEALTH AND LONGEVITY have increased phenomenally since the turn of the century by whatever means they are measured. A child born in 1900 had a life expectation of a little less than fifty years. Six decades later, an infant could expect to live nearly seventy years. Progress in extending the average length of life was accelerated by the quickened tempo of advances in preventive and curative medicine, and in environmental sanitation. The progress of this century followed upon an increase before 1900 in the expectation of life at birth which, while significant, nevertheless was only about half as much as that achieved in the succeeding half-century.

In the work of Louis Pasteur, the nineteenth century saw the establishment of the germ theory of disease and a realization of the importance of sanitation. Modern medicine dawned with the application of inquiry, research, and the experimental method to the ills that beset mankind. The actual treatment of disease itself had, in the previous centuries, given an empirical knowledge of medicine. More important to the scientific development of medicine are the fundamental inquiries made possible by those who study and experiment with disease rather than treat it as practitioners.

Reinforcing the physicians, surgeons, and other specialists, the century has produced an extraordinary body of medical scientists, responsible for the tools of scientific medicine, that has created

Dr. Walter Reed

an understanding of disease and an array of drugs far beyond the hopes of the past.

In 1900 medical treatment consisted largely of tonics, purgatives, diaphoretics, and analgesics. Such remedies had come into use as a result of empirical observation. The idea of achieving a radical cure of disease rather than merely an alleviation of symptoms was hardly entertained. Many of the infectious diseases were rampant. Epidemics virtually ravaged sections of the population. For instance, as late as 1891 the death rate from typhoid fever in Chicago reached 172 per 100,000 of population, a rate exceeding all but one of the death categories in America's mid-century. Contrast this with the fact that the last major epidemic in the United States was the influenza pandemic of 1918-19.

One of the most famous research groups ever established was that headed by Drs. Walter Reed, Jesse W. Lazear (a martyr to the research), and James Carroll. In 1900 they proved beyond a doubt that yellow fever is transmitted by a particular species of mosquito. This was the midpoint of a twenty-year period of significant discoveries in the field of medical entomology. During this

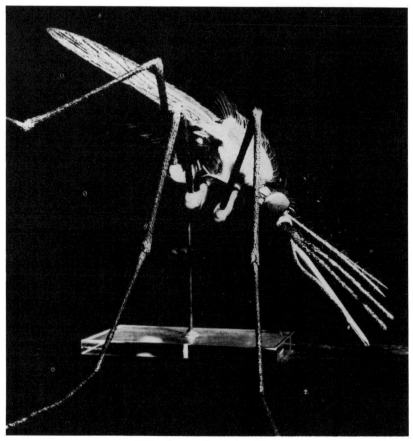

Malaria-carrying mosquito.

time, insects were unmasked as carriers of protozoan and worm diseases that plague especially the tropical areas.

By the turn of the century, giant steps had been made in tracking down the insect hosts of elephantiasis, malaria, nagana, and Texas cattle fever. Scientists in the following decades found that tsetse flies carried the graceful trypanosomes of Rhodesian and Gambian sleeping sickness, and body lice transmitted typhus fever, relapsing fever, and dog tapeworm. Ticks were established as the insect vectors in spirochetosis of chickens, African relapsing fever, and Rocky Mountain spotted fever, while kissing bugs or conenose bugs were indicated in Brazilian trypanosomiasis or Chagas disease. Blood-sucking gnats, flies, and fleas were added to the list of intermediate hosts.

The conquest of infection is a tribute not only to discovery of the cause of infection, but also to the development and utilization of immunization methods and the application of sanitation on a wide scale. By these various methods, many of the great plagues of all time have been brought under such rational and effective treatment that they can be considered to have been conquered. The list of such diseases includes puerperal fever, laryngitis, typhoid, typhus, dysentery, gonorrhea, syphilis, pernicious anemia, myxedema, scurvy, and rickets.

Joining the smallpox vaccination achievement of the eighteenth century, typhoid vaccine was developed before World War I. Its widespread use demonstrated its effectiveness during the First World War. Today, in many parts of the world, typhoid is so rare that a case attracts medical students and even doctors who have never seen it. Immunization against diphtheria is applied to children when they are very young, and there has been a virtual disappearance of this illness in most large communities that have practiced such systematic protection. "Shots" to immunize against tetanus are now given both in armies and in civilian life, eliminating the terror of lockjaw. Typhus has been subdued as a disease

Testing relative merit of two repellants on mosquitoes.

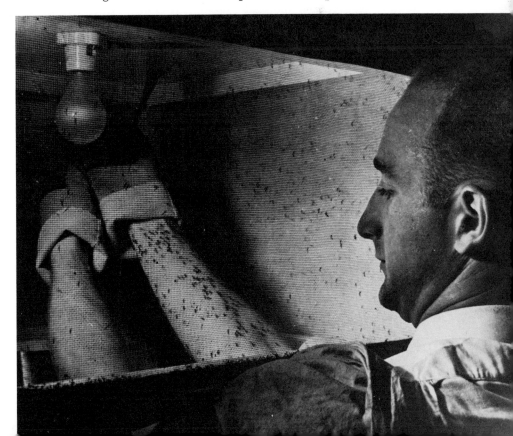

of war and disaster through a combination of vaccination and the use of insecticides to curb the body lice that carry it.

The tropics have lost one of their great dangers through vaccination against yellow fever. To the list of diseases against which protection can be obtained have been added whooping cough, tuberculosis, poliomyelitis, measles, and even influenza, despite its seemingly changing nature.

In another kind of attack on disease, the chemist has used organic chemistry to synthesize artificial remedies which deal with infectious agents. The first chemotherapeutic bullets were fired in 1909 when Paul Ehrlich and his school developed a remedy for syphilis. But the first third of the century passed with successes that were limited largely to the treatment of parasitic plagues in tropical regions. Plasmochin and atabrine for malaria, germanin and tryparasamide for sleeping sickness, emetine and yatren for amoebiasis, tartar emetic for leishmaniasis and blood flukes, gentian violet for Chinese liver flukes and strongyloidiasis were all developed before 1933. Insecticides and mosquito abatement campaigns supplemented the new drugs.

Immunology seemed to be the hope of curbing the bacterial infections predominant in temperate climates. Then the sulfonamide drugs, which became available shortly before World War II, ushered in an era of chemotherapy which has had more significant and more rapid effects than any similar achievement. The sulfonamide drugs were effective against pneumonia, puerperal

Paul Ehrlich (1854-1915), German medical research worker, a great pioneer and experimental genius in the application of chemistry to biological and medical science, who was awarded Nobel prize in medicine in 1908.

Disulfanilamide crystals—Sulfanilamide, as the first sulfa drug, ushered in the new era of chemotherapy. Sulfanilamide is a peculiarly effective weapon against members of the streptococcus family. A German scientist, Dr. G. Domagk, discovered this when he tried Prontosil for treatment of streptococcus infections in mice. Prontosil, a patented, ink-red dye, also available in the form of flat white pills, has as one of its chemical constituents sulfanilamide.

fever, meningitis and gonorrhea. Sufferers from a whole range of common or bacterial infections benefited from this great advance.

A very few years later, penicillin, rapidly developed from laboratory experiment to large-scale production under the urgency of war, produced effective results against many of the bacterial diseases untouched by the sulfonamides, which it superseded. Penicillin was followed by other antibiotics, both naturally produced and artificially synthesized. Streptomycin, chloromycetin, and aureomycin cured diseases against which penicillin was

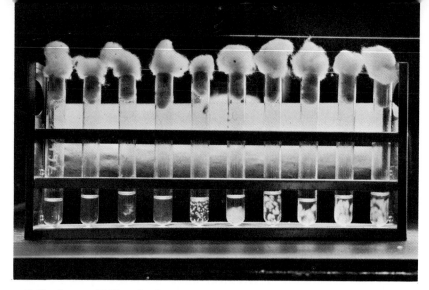

Sulfa drugs—Fifth tube from left, the control in the test for streptococcal resistance to sulfa drugs shows streptococci growing without any sulfa drug in the special medium prepared at the National Naval Medical Center, Bethesda, Md. The first four tubes at the left show how the addition of sulfa drug kills streptococci. The tubes to the right of the control illustrate streptococci growing even after the sulfa drug has been added, showing that germs in these tubes are sulfa drug-resistant.

not effective. The newer antibiotics even checked some virus diseases.

The search for new antibiotics, manufactured by chemists or extracted from natural substances, continues because man's enemies, the bacteria, are constantly changing in their struggle for survival, becoming able, through evolution, to live in the presence of their chemical enemies.

Some human ills are caused by the lack of substances in our food and our bodies. The classic case of deficiency in the diet is scurvy, due to lack of vitamin C. Several centuries ago, successful treatment of scurvy with fresh fruit and vegetables was discovered, only to be lost and rediscovered in later years. Not until the first decade of the century passed was the name vitamin applied to such accessory factors in nutrition. Lack of vitamin D, contained classically in cod-liver oil, causes rickets, while other vitamins, responsible for different aspects of growth and metabolism, have been chemically isolated and identified in the years between the two world wars. The treatment of pernicious anemia, which first consisted of eating liver, later the use of vitamin B-12, is another triumph of vitamin therapy.

Hormones, or glandular secretions, obtained from slaughtered animals or made synthetically, have been isolated and used therapeutically. In this class are thyroid extracts, adrenalin, post-pituitary fractions, insulin for the treatment of diabetes, para-thyroid hormones, the various sex hormones, the adreno-cortical hormones and anterior pituitary hormones. Such replacement therapy keeps thousands in health who otherwise would have died.

The pioneering life-saving discovery of insulin for diabetes, more than a generation ago, has received reinforcements. To replace or at least supplement this hormone which must be given by injection, there are now substances with similar effects that can be taken by mouth. Newer forms of the cortical steroids have shown much promise in the treatment of arthritis.

The pharmaceutical industry has produced the tranquilizers, chlorpromazine and reserpine, drugs that calm the temperament or elevate the mood and energize the psyche. Although not yet a major treatment for mental illness, some of these chemical modi-fiers of human personality may be pointing the way toward con-

A storehouse of antibiotic cultures used in research. Research and Development Department, Terre Haute, Ind.

COMMERCIAL SOLVENTS CORPORATION

trol of psychoses. At least they allow the mentally ill to live more satisfactorily with themselves and those around them. The breakthrough in the understanding of mental disease has not yet occurred, but with increasing appreciation of the problem and more research being devoted to it may come fundamental knowledge in this field as there has in other areas of disease.

Although phenomenal strides have been made in eliminating disease, the major cause of death in 1900 remains unconquered and still reigns as the king of killers after six decades. Cardiovascular-renal diseases were responsible for 55 per cent of total deaths in 1958. They took more lives in proportion to population than they did at the century's turn. Formerly, one of the deterrents to investigation of the problem of heart attack was a common attitude that it was a consequence of old age, and that very little could be done about it. Once this misconception was realized, research began in earnest.

At present, heart valves can be widened by surgical correction, and sections of dangerously weak and bulging arteries, known as aneurysms, can be replaced by special plastic tubing or by arterial transplants. Artificial heart-lung machines circulate and oxygenate a patient's blood during "open heart" operations in which the heart can be stopped for as long as sixty minutes. There is hope

Dr. F. G. Banting, discoverer of insulin for diabetes.

Heart-lung machine—Dr. John Ross, Jr., Cardiac Surgical Service, National Institutes of Health, Bethesda, Md., holds up the two tubes that connect the Melrose type heart-lung bypass machine to the human body.

that an experimental, electrically driven artificial heart, permanently implanted in the patient, will be ready for use within the foreseeable future.

For all the cures, prevention is far more valuable. Through the use of the electrocardiograph, first manufactured in the United States in 1923, the variations of electricity passing over the heart trace out a picture that can be used as a rapid evaluation of the health of the heart at a given time. Other small devices can look into the heart without surgery or "hear" extremely faint heart murmurs. Mountains of statistical correlations have been compiled so that it is now possible to estimate an individual's susceptibility to atherosclerosis and arteriosclerosis by considering his blood pressure and certain lipoproteins.

Cancer, like cardiovascular-renal disease, is increasing in incidence, and now ranks as the second-most frequent cause of death.

The methods by which cancer spreads through the body are known, but the why and how of the disease are still unknown. Each year viruses become more suspect as a cause of cancer. Their carcinogenic action in some laboratory animals has been shown, but such activity in man is not a proved fact. Medication consists of surgical removal of malignant tumors, irradiation with X-rays, and therapeutic use of radioactive isotopes, such as iridium-192 and cobalt-60, and use of about twenty drugs to combat growth of tumors.

The search for the cure and cause of cancer is the greatest medical research effort the world has ever seen. Almost every idea and promising lead are being tested by scientists armed with adequate laboratories amply financed, by government, foundations, and public fund-raising. Two approaches are being tried, with the hope that one or both will yield results that can be applied clinically to saving human lives by the prevention or cure of malignancies.

The varieties of cancer are legion, with some entities of the diseases differing so much from others that eventually they will not even be considered in the same class. There are about twenty main types and two hundred individual kinds of malignant tumors. Some cancers, such as that of the prostate (treated with sex hormones), are curable if caught early enough; others have a very discouraging prognosis even if detected early in their course.

A far cry from the operating room of the last century is today's modern setting with its overhead sterilizing lamps and transfusion bottles. Many of the surgical techniques of today are based on casual experiments of the nineteenth century. Blood transfusion was more or less a dangerous experimental novelty, and the value of plasma as well as whole blood was unknown until 1939. Intravenous anaesthesia was viewed with distrust until 1903, when the value of the barbiturates came into focus. Modern practice uses muscle relaxants in combination with light local or general anaesthesia for greater total safety to the patient.

The injuries of war necessitated a new outlook on trauma and deformity. From the metal plates, screws, nails, and pins used as bone replacement in 1917, prosthesis has matured to replacing entire hip joints and arteries with inorganic substitutes. Plastic and cosmetic surgery developed remarkably under the impetus of the need to remedy war injuries. Burns are now considered open wounds, and the tannic acid treatment has been abandoned in favor of skin grafts and the modified exposure treatment.

Significant developments in surgery include those in tissue transplantation. Although the mechanics of the operation may be relatively simple, the antibody response on the part of the host prevents homografts of all tissues. Even so, bone, skin, arteries, eye corneas, ovaries, adrenal and parathyroid glands have been transplanted. Some tissues can even be taken from persons who have just died and then stored in "banks" for future use.

Keeping pace with discoveries of causes and cures are a wealth of laboratory tests to aid the physician in diagnosing the illness and choosing the best treatment. Chemical and microscopic procedures for examination of body fluids, tissues, and waste products are so streamlined that it is now possible to determine pathology during the course of a surgical operation.

Without electronic equipment and specialized instruments such rapid analysis would be impossible. The medical field is rapidly approaching full utilization of the technical products of the modern age. High speed centrifuges, electron microscopes, and simple blood-counting chambers are all twentieth century innovations. Within a few years, medical libraries will begin transferring information to high-speed digital computers. They will store patient records, read and abstract medical literature, compile histories and statistics of diseases and their treatment, analyze wave forms from electrocardiographs, and perform routine laboratory duties that do not require subjective judgment.

The reverse of public health and preventive medicine is germ warfare. During World War I saboteurs inoculated horses and cattle, designated for shipment to the Allies, with disease-producing bacteria. But it was not until the beginning of the Second World War that the destructive potential of biological agents was fully considered. At that time, facilities were established for research and experimentation on pathogenic agents on a scale never before possible.

Researchers found methods for large-scale production and dispersion of bacteria, fungi, viruses, rickettsiae, and toxic agents from living organisms. They studied possible use of infected insect vectors and disease-carrying rodents. Any organism that can be used to cause disease or death in man, animals, or plants is considered in biological warfare.

Although both sides involved in World War II had stockpiles of this type of weapon, neither side exploited it. So devastating could be the consequence of mass dissemination of cholera, smallpox, typhus, and plague, that it has been likened to the atom bomb as an agent for destruction. In actual fact, biological warfare in some form is centuries old, and even on the modern scale it is not absolute.

Whatever is known of disease and debility is only a small part of what is still to be discovered. Research groups, working as independent organizations or in colleges, pharmaceutical companies, and hospitals, cannot do all that needs to be done. The nation's annual output of physicians, dentists, nurses, pharmacists, and technicians barely keeps pace with the growing population.

The layman has been encouraged to take a certain amount of responsibility in guarding his own health. Gradually the public has been educated to the importance of sanitation, quarantine, immunization, balanced diet, and early medication. For some of the major diseases, the average person has learned to recognize the danger signs—the lumps that continue to grow, and limbs that feel heavy during exertion.

For other ills, neither the physician nor the researcher has the answer. Diseases such as leprosy, muscular dystrophy, multiple sclerosis, and arthritis are tragic not because they kill, but because they twist and cripple the body. New diseases are constantly cropping up. Some are mutations of pathogenic agents that have survived attacks by synthetic drugs.

Underlying the whole problem of health, disease, and death is the basic unit of life, the cell. There is promise that, in the future, research may be able to fathom its workings and answer the biggest question of all: What is life? When it is known what sparks vital activity and differentiates the living from the dead, many medical mysteries will be unraveled, and basic factors in illness understood.

Along man's long and devious journey to such knowledge there will be inspiring and rewarding findings that will solve some of the problems relating to the mechanisms of disease. The basic fundamental inquiries so necessary to scientific progress are sure to pay their way by illuminating facts of unexpected relevance to human existence.

THE
POPULATION
EXPLOSION

EVERY MORNING there are at least 100,000 more mouths that must be fed and bodies that must be clothed on the face of the earth. This is the extraordinary explosion of population that, in this century, is pitting humanity's numbers against the earth's resources.

This almost frightening increase in the number of people in the world is no new and unpredicted phenomenon. In 1798, Malthus recognized the oncoming danger, although, like most prophets, he predicted neither the details nor some of the consequences of science's impact on the onrush of population.

A combination of factors has made Malthus' dire predictions of the population outrunning food slower of fulfillment than he had imagined. The application of science to agriculture vastly increased the amount of food available, and thus postponed the dangers which he foresaw. On the other hand, the extraordinary increase in the length of human life and the conquest of plagues have allowed such increases in numbers of people that, even with added food resources, the world is again faced with the danger of future famine.

The world has approximately 2,750,000,000 population. The population is currently increasing at an explosive rate which causes it to double every forty-five years.

It seems inevitable that the number of human beings on earth

T. R. Malthus

will increase to at least 5,500,000,000 and perhaps as many as 6,000,000,000 by the end of the century. Those who have studied this phenomenon see nothing ahead at the moment that will stop this trend.

Population experts of the United Nations, who took a look backward in history, have found that it required 200,000 years for the world to acquire its present population. About the time of Christ, the earth had its first quarter billion people, and it took 198,000 years, according to the experts, for the world population to arrive at this figure. To double this to half a billion took some sixteen centuries, doubling from that to a billion the next 250 years, between 1600 and 1850. The population doubled again to two billion, reaching this point in about 1930.

It is not very helpful to project the population growth too far in the future. Some statisticians have speculated that, if the present population growth rate should continue for seven centuries, the entire fifty-two million square miles of the planet's dry land, including desert wastes, arctic tundra, and mountain vastnesses, would afford only one square foot of living space for each human being hypothetically on the earth. Before this happened there would undoubtedly come into play the Malthus principle, which is that population always increases up to the means of existence.

It seems rather unlikely that the means of existence would multiply to such an extent as to allow this extraordinary increase, although technology and applied science have increased both food and health so that the earth can support more people than ever imagined.

In the previous twenty centuries, populations were largely held in check by plagues and famines. The high death rate can be vividly emphasized by stating that, if today we had the death rates of 150 years ago, chances are that you would not have survived to be reading this. One hundred and fifty years ago almost half the children born all over the world died before they reached maturity.

Although the earlier accomplishments in medicine by Jenner, Pasteur, Lister, and other pioneers of scientific medicine began the reduction in death rates and the lengthening of life, wonder drugs and the extraordinary insecticides of the present century have primarily brought about the dramatic control of disease that reduced death rates by about half in the space of a very few years. Population growth has speeded astoundingly in this century, not because of an increase in birth rates, but because of the sudden decline in death rates caused by the conquest of disease.

In some underdeveloped countries today the birth rate remains at forty-five per thousand per year, while the death rate has dropped to about twenty-five. This causes a natural increase of twenty, an annual growth of 2 per cent a year. A banker would not be happy about such a compound interest rate of 2 per cent, but it threatens bankruptcy to a world from the population standpoint.

The pressure of population is greatest where peoples and economies are least able to adjust themselves to take care of this overburden of people. And, while situations in such countries as Ceylon, India, and Indonesia are most pressing, the specter of overpopulation threatens the whole world, the most advanced countries and the underdeveloped areas alike. If a population explosion, caused by low death rates and high birth rates, continues into the future, there seems to be little hope of improving the living standards of well over half the world's people.

The surpluses of food crops in the United States, and the economic embarrassment that they cause, give a distorted picture of

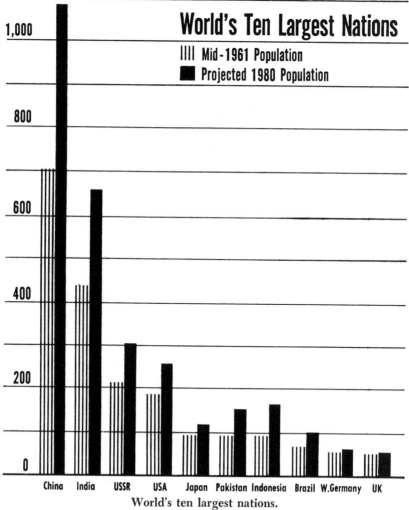

World's ten largest nations.

the ability of the world to produce food for its accelerating population. There still is hunger, particularly for the protein and protective foods, in many parts of the world despite the American overabundance of calories.

The world can undoubtedly produce more food, clothing, shelter, and even luxurious conveniences for an increasing population, but there is a limit to what the earth can provide.

The possibility of obtaining more resources for human living through applications of atomic energy, farming the oceans for food, solving the possible utilization of the sun's energy more efficiently by discoveries that outdo the green leaf, and other such means of creating more resources may postpone the universal tendency of population to outrun the means of existence. But this will be merely temporary if high birth rates continue.

Man-made restrictions on the size of world population is the solution which is urged by many.

Some nations have already achieved a degree of control over population growth rates. One of these is Japan, perhaps the most crowded country in Asia. Its spectacular decline in birth rate from 34.3 in 1947 to 17.2 in 1957 is cited by those who feel this population explosion may be checked. The Japanese are intensely aware of the danger of overpopulation and, after World War II, brought contraceptives into widespread use, and legalized abortion and sterilization. Added to these factors, a natural decrease in birth rate seems to have brought about the amazing decline. Whether this experiment will be repeated in other parts of the world is a question for the future.

The United States at mid-century was undergoing some of the consequences of population pressure. The rapid growth and movement of the population contributed to a deteriorating educational system, overcrowded suburban areas, decaying central cities, vanishing water supplies, and increased taxes.

The control of the world's population explosion involves more than merely persuading people not to have children. For the good of the world, it is a matter of quality as well as quantity. Millions of couples whose potential progeny would be a great asset to the world refrain from having children for various reasons, some of them economic. Parallel to any campaign to reduce the family size, many population experts feel that larger families should be encouraged for those of desirable inheritance who are economi-

Francis Galton

cally able to raise their children so that they are well supported
and well educated. For many thousands of husbands and wives,
more than generally realized, studies show that the problem is not
to keep from having children but to be able to have them. Studies
in human fertility are just as important in increasing fertility as
in limiting conception.

In all times before this century, the major control factor in
population has been natural selection. It has eliminated the weak
and the defective. Under present conditions, with ninety-five out
of one hundred children born alive surviving to the middle of
their reproductive period, death has lost its historic function of
improving the race and protecting it from deterioration. That is
the reason that selection by birth rather than elimination by death
has become an advocated method of improving the human race.
Women no longer need to have as many children as possible to
have the individual family survive, as was the case in previous
centuries when many of those born would be wasted by an early
death.

The discoveries in heredity made by Mendel and his followers through experiments on plants and animals have logically given a scientific basis to the eugenics movement founded earlier by Galton. The twentieth century saw the abuse of eugenics by those who believed they belonged to a superior race. Laws were passed providing for the so-called eugenic sterilization of criminals in an attempt to free the world of crime. The worst of these movements found their climax under Hitler, who combined it for purposes of political conquest with genocide, murdering millions.

It seemed obvious by mid-century that something would have to be done to limit the growth of the world's population. It was not evident, however, that man knew enough to make birth selections favoring genetic capacities for intelligence, farsightedness, or character. In the earliest days, when death controlled those who were to reproduce and people the earth, the man who was brave and strong kept the saber-toothed tiger from killing his young, the patient and the farseeing saved food against the winter, the intelligent made better weapons and used them more artfully.

Medical research is today learning about the method of inheritance of human defects and qualities, so that prospective parents can know their potentialities as producers of future generations.

As birth selection becomes more prevalent than it is in the United States during the present era, there is confidence that a combination of growing knowledge of human heredity and a sense of responsibility among the groups presumably most capable and "fit" will cause an upgrading in the ability and the effectiveness, intellectually and physically, of the population.

To the rest of the world where the population problem is even more serious, the experience and knowledge worked out largely in the Western world will prove of use in guiding and motivating the building of future populations.

As is widely recognized, not enough is known about the population problem to be completely sure of ways to handle it. To regulate births of the future effectively, both in the case of individual couples and upon a national scale, requires more understanding of the basic physiology of reproduction than is presently available. A safe, cheap, and positive method of preventing conception temporarily is a critical necessity. This does not exist, despite the encouraging research and large-scale trials that have been made of various chemicals. New inquiries leading to a scientific basis for birth regulation are just as much needed as researches on how to increase the effectiveness of existing food supplies and how to develop new scientific and technological knowledge that will give increased food production from neglected and untapped world resources.

The population explosion applies to other creatures of the earth than man himself. Disease germs, and even the microorganisms useful to man, need to be controlled.

In the case of livestock raised for food, the cattleman exercises the most rigorous kind of birth regulation to serve human needs. As regards pests of various sorts, they can be exterminated or kept at a desired level. The human population is to us the most important facet of the living world and other forms of life on the earth must be understood and controlled to serve human purposes.

Statistical facts on the extent and location of the growth of population are in many instances quite unsatisfactory, although demographers have more accurate knowledge than they have had in the past decades. Even in the twentieth century, it is probable that population figures are inaccurate by many millions. Monetary figures are much more accurate and, in the long run, much less important.

It would be curious to see what the experts of the future say about the figures and fears that are being expressed about the world's peoples.

Are we too sanguine, or too pessimistic? Are pregnant facts that will be so plain to the future being overlooked in our rush of today?

Crowded living conditions in slums.

CIVILIZATIONS
AND
PEOPLES

THE DEMONSTRATION of the evolution of all life on earth, including that of the human race, was an outstanding accomplishment of the nineteenth century. Darwin's great work and the discovery of the record of the rocks showed that the rise of plants and animals through the geologic eras was continuous and gradual, giving no place for the idea of special creation of either man or other living forms. Special creation, as told in Genesis or numerous other religious accounts, was relegated to the realm of fanciful legend.

The emotionally satisfying assumption that man is something special, created by a very different process than the rest of the earth, died hard. Part of the special creation theory of man extends to the doctrine of racism: the assumption that one kind or group of the human race, usually the one to which the advocate belongs, is better, more richly endowed, and generally superior to the rest of mankind.

The anti-evolution trial at Dayton, Tennessee, in 1925, was a desperate defense by those who believed literally in the King James version of the Bible, a sort of back-to-the-wall stand of anti-biological literalism in theology. The murder of millions of Jews during World War II and Hitlerism's racist national creed were die-hard support of the illusion of race superiority. The liberation of native peoples and the creation of new nations out of colonial dependencies twenty years later brought to world attention, through armed conflict and peaceful settlement, both the differences in peoples and their political and cultural equalities. Where peoples of different skin color and different cultural traditions are living in the same area, the basic conflict between the so-called races continues, as for instance "Apartheid" in South Africa, and the differences between the whites and Negroes in other parts of the Dark Continent, as well as in parts of the United States.

The idea of superiority of one kind of man over another is exemplified by the institution of human slavery, which existed as recently as a hundred years ago in the United States, although now virtually extinct in the world. While not all slavery or other differences for discrimination were based on ethnic groups, these were common classifications easily distinguished.

The concept of culture has dominated the study of mankind in this century. Culture is a society's customs, traditions, tools, and ways of thinking. It has become increasingly evident that it plays an overpowering part in the development of human beings. This idea has guided anthropological studies both of men known from fossil records and in living groups. The continuity and the differences in culture have motivated the digging into deeper layers of the earth to discover earlier forms of man and his progenitors. They have spurred the excavation of ancient cities. They have instigated the ethnological inquiries into the differences in customs, actions, and thinking of today's ethnic groups, primitive and industrially advanced.

The overthrow of the parochial idea of superiority of the culture in which one was born and raised is perhaps the most important development in anthropology and ethnology today. We have a very natural tendency to consider what our own civilization does the best. And we compare other civilizations, past and present, with our own as a standard. Viewing the wide expanse of animal and plant life which has evolved on our planet, we find many thousands of different species of extraordinary diversity. This reminds us that it is not surprising to have different cultures within the human race, and that some of them have attributes superior to others. There is not necessarily any one culture which has complete "God-given" superiority.

Man, the talking, tool-using, thinking, and record-making dominant creature upon the earth has had his ancestry traced back at least ten million years. The biological history of man and his immediate fossil ancestors has been discovered in large part in this century. The human family tree is visible in its broad outlines, although future research will need to fill in gaps. There is still need for careful exploration into the fossil record once chance or carefully planned excavation has revealed an early progenitor enclosed in the earth's layers.

The rise of mankind through the long evolutionary record begins in the primordial slime of the young earth when, somehow or other, life began. Through the millennia and finally down the path of vertebrates, the primates appeared, in the biological order of which Homo sapiens is the most advanced species. In the geological time known as Late Tertiary there were slender little apelike creatures, small hominids, which, although primitive, had

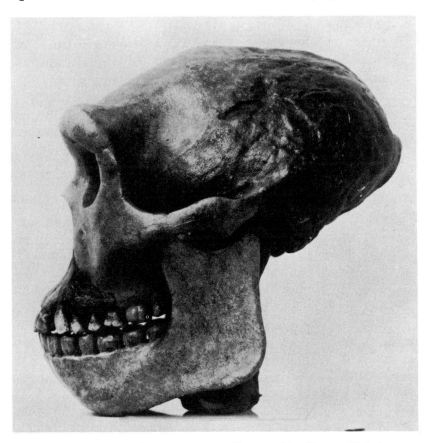

Pithecanthropus, the Java ape-man discovered by Eugene Dubois.

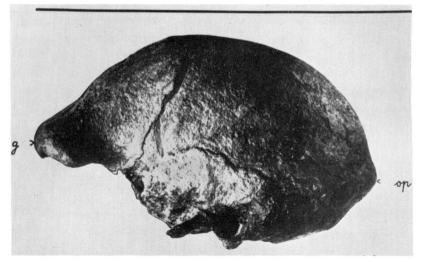

Pithecanthropus von Java

within them the possibility of evolving into a being who could stand erect and move about standing up. Many centuries passed and these creatures became what are known as Australopithecinae. Again after many centuries this creature became man-like with bigger brain and cranial refinement. This was Pithecanthropus, the Java ape-man discovered by Eugene Dubois, which at the turn of the century was still a subject of acute controversy, although it had been discovered in central Java a decade earlier. An anthropological brother to Pithecanthropus is Sinanthropus or Peking Man, represented by skull and teeth discovered in the latter half of the 1920's. The bones themselves—jaws, skull, and teeth—disappeared during World War II in the hands of the Japanese, an occurrence which has become one of the mystery stories of anthropology. Sinanthropus Pekinensis won its place in the rise of mankind nonetheless.

Thus one of the human cradles seems to have been in the Far East. Farther west there was unearthed evidence of men, who might have been much like the Peking and the Java men, occupying North Africa at about the same time. An important finding in South Africa is Australopithecus which essentially had the teeth, jaws, hips, and posture of man, along with a brain the size of gorillas and big chimpanzees.

From finds made during the twentieth century it became evident that many fossils, including bones left by cannibals, skulls, jaws, and even fossil footprints, pointed to another experimentation in human evolution that was widespread over most of Europe, North Africa, and even the Near East and Central Asia. These were Neanderthalers, big-faced, large-skulled, and bony-browed, with brains essentially as large as those of today. But they were a sideline in human evolution. Modern man is not descended from them. Neanderthal Man was dominant in the Ice Ages, arriving in the Third Interglacial and continuing into the Fourth Glacial times, perhaps fifty thousand to seventy thousand years ago.

It has taken longer than previously credited for the kind of people now on earth to rise to become what we know as modern man. Present evidence indicates that man and his cultures extend beyond two million years into the past.

Radioactive dating has given new time determinations for human ancestors and evolution in the dim anthropological past. The "clock" or dating method measures the amount of the element argon in rocks to determine their age. This element is formed by radioactive disintegration from potassium, and the ratio of these two elements therefore allows computation of age.

The age of the earliest skeletal remains, generally conceded "human," those of Zinjanthropus discovered in Olduvai Gorge, Tanganyika, was found to be 1,750,000 years when determined by the potassium-argon method.

Homo sapiens, modern man, of which all living men constitute a single kind, arrived about the year 35,000 B.C. He stems from what are known as Cro-Magnon men, first discovered in the nineteenth century from their fossil remains. In recent years it has been recognized that our Homo sapiens existed well back into the Pleistocene, and long before that his ancestors must have been set off from all other forms of man-like creatures living or extinct.

The importance of 35,000 B.C. as the great turning point in the rise of modern man may possibly be a misleading conception in the minds of some anthropologists, but it is accepted that about that time Homo sapiens was widely spread in the Old World and entering the New World as well. There was a human flow to the Americas and the Pacific.

The human people of the earth with their differences—Hottentots, Bushmen, Negroes, Mongolians, Eskimos and Indians, Australians, and various variations of whites and off-whites—all seem to have come from the same source, changed and modified

Dr. L. S. B. Leakey, of the Coryndon Museum, Nairobi, Kenya, holds a cast of his find of the first skull of Chellean man, who lived about 400,000 years ago in East Africa. On the table are casts of his finds of skull parts of an adult and a child who lived there more than 600,000 years ago. The child's teeth (next to the skull parts) indicate he (or she) was eleven years old at the time of death; he was killed by a blow on the head.

through centuries upon centuries. The study of existing populations and their characteristics has begun to sort out racial relationships. Experimental genetics is not very helpful because human
lives are long, generations mature slowly, and the human chromosomes are numerous and ill-explored. It is not possible to conduct
experiments on human beings as biologists do on fruit flies or
plants. Some idea of racial relationships have been obtained from
various blood types, but this type of research as to origins and
racial relationships among human stock has hardly begun. From
study of language as well, something should be learned about the
anthropological origins of people.

The exact lines of ascent of the kinds of men have not emerged
with assurance from the medley of human fossils that anthropologists have assembled. Most widely accepted is the idea that
modern man in all his variations has come from the Cro-Magnons,
although early in the century one theory proposed that moderns
did have Neanderthal ancestors who themselves were descendants
of Java Man. Still another theory of human descent, less widely
held now than it was in the early part of this century, claimed
that Java Man gave rise to Australians, the Peking Man to Mongolians, Rhodesian Man to Africans, and the peoples represented
by the Skhul and Tabun skulls to Eurasians through the Cro-
Magnons. These strivings to discover how human beings arose
through the millennia and mists of pre-history will undoubtedly
continue through the rest of the century. More remains of ancient
man will be found by accident or by planned excavations.

Some of the preconceptions, theories, and even fossils themselves will be toppled from their place, just as the famous Piltdown Man rose and fell. Unearthed in 1912 from a British gravel
pit, it was regarded as an authentic human relic until exposed in
1953 as a hoax, a planted artifact that was so cleverly forged that
it fooled the experts for some four decades. Eoanthropus, as Piltdown Man was named, was not a complete loss to science, although bogus and repudiated. It did give testimony to the
advances in the knowledge of anthropological methods of determining what is correct and what is not. Tests for fluorine content,
used in the exposure of the Piltdown fraud, showed that the
artifact had too little of this element to support its antiquity.
Another branch of science thus came to the aid of anthropology.

Even before the rise of our ancestors, called by anthropologists

Maya clay figurine from Jaina, Campeche, Mexico.

Model of earliest known Maya temple now exhibited at Chicago Natural History Museum. The original structure, erected about 100 B.C., was excavated by the Carnegie Institution of Washington in the Guatemalan jungle at Uaxactun.

Homo sapiens, there were toolmakers. Hand-axes were fashioned out of stone and flint tools were flaked. Archaeologists have found these throughout a vast area of the African and West Eurasian continents. They were made about 250,000 years ago by wandering ancient men, hunters, gatherers of food, and scavengers of what existed wild in the territory over which they exercised control as the most intelligent animal in creation. When the modern physical type of man appeared some 50,000 years ago, tool making improved. There is evidence in the record of pre-history that there was more systematic collection of food and that hunting was organized more effectively, supplementing the simple gathering and hit-or-miss utilization of what was found wild in the land.

In the present century more and more facts have been assembled by archaeological explorations in which botanists, zoologists, and geologists collaborated. Evidence has been found of the beginning of agricultural evolution about ten thousand years ago. Food was grown, animals were domesticated, plants were culti-

Pharaoh Tutankhamon of Egypt

vated, and people gathered in villages to make this first approach to agriculture easier and more effective.

The record of the rise of agriculture is most clearly known from the studies in southwestern Asia, but independently the Mayas in Mexico and the Incas in Peru, both from the same source perhaps, made their discoveries of agriculture in the course of building their amazing civilizations.

In these times so much closer to the present than the evolutionary beginnings of mankind, extensive civilizations and cities rose, existed, and decayed in such places as the fertile plains of Mesopotamia and the jungles of ancient Mexico. As we have come to realize in recent years, most of the great monuments that have aroused archaeological interest as targets for study and excavation had their origin and reason for being in the need to worship and propitiate fearful gods.

For several hundred years before our century, ancient cities were studied and pillaged, treasures were carried to foreign lands, and some realization was obtained about the antiquity and the long-continued development of ancient pre-history.

To mention the most spectacular archaeological explorations of

Statues of Rameses II in Temple of Luxor, Egypt.

ARTHUR S. RIGGS

this century in which American scientists participated: Hiram Bingham discovered the old Inca fortresses of Machu Picchu and Vitcos around Cuzco, Peru. The Carnegie Institution explored and restored Mayan cities rescued from the jungle. Pueblo Bonito in New Mexico was unearthed. The Carnarvon Expedition digging near Luxor in the Valley of the Kings in Egypt made discoveries of the tomb of Tutankhamen, the richness of which fascinated the American public. The Mexican archaeologist, Alfonso Caso, discovered on Monte Alban near Oaxaca in Mexico, the richest gold treasure ever found in Middle America. Another Mexican, Alberto Ruz, excavated the Temple of the Inscriptions at

One-piece pyramid and temple of Malinalco, State of Mexico, excavated by José García Payón, 1936.

Xochicolco, Mexico (close-up).

Xochicolco, Mexico.

Great temple at Tikal, Guatemala, now overgrown with foliage.

The University Museum of the University of Pennsylvania will partially restore Tikal.

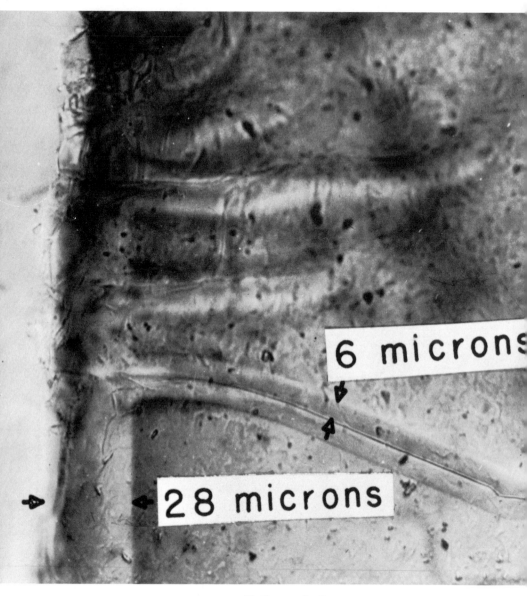

6 microns

28 microns

Dating methods.

Palenque, discovering inside the tomb of a ruler. Because of their relationship to the Bible and the light they shed on New Testament origins, Hebrew scrolls in jars and clay vessels, found by a Bedouin in a cave north of the Dead Sea, created great interest.

Two new archaeological techniques emerged in recent years. Incidental to aerial exploration for military purposes, it was demonstrated that the camera is able to see configurations and traces of old roads and fortifications that the observer on the ground could not detect.

A great contribution from physics and atomic science was W. F. Libby's development of a method for determining the age of organic remains by means of the rate of disintegration of radio-isotope carbon-14. This achievement, which won Dr. Libby the Nobel Prize in physics, gave archaeology its first reliable measure of time, good to an antiquity of something like thirty thousand years.

As man remakes the earth with dams that flood many acres, with roads that level hills and valleys, with subdivisions that bull-doze into sameness landscapes unchanged for generations, there has been some appreciation of the record that is likely to be destroyed. Archaeologists were supported and encouraged to capture the record of the past before the onslaught of modern civilization rearranges it. As a result, the future may not be totally ignorant of the past.

FABIAN BACHRACH

Dr. Willard F. Libby, Nobel Prize winner.

Mitla, Mexico.

Mitla, Mexico.

MIND
AND
EMOTIONS

MAN IS A thinking, planning, and doing entity distinct from the lower animals, even the other primates. He owes this superiority and difference to his brain and what is called "mind." Human attributes reside largely in the processes and spoken expression of thought, and in the effect of emotion and behavior.

Human physiology, biochemistry, and complex operations of the human body, which control health and disease, are strikingly akin to the life processes of other animals. If we could communicate more effectively with the lower animals, we would probably find that their minds and emotions are more nearly parallel to our own than we generally realize. While there can be some exploration in an experiment with animals of basic processes of learning, and even emotion and behavior, for the most part man has to be his own experimental animal in the fields of psychology and psychiatry.

The twentieth century has been an era of experiment, advance, and understanding in the human mental processes and emotions, in health and disease. Progress in the mental realm and its effect upon human beings has run the gamut from Freud and psychoanalysis to the extraordinary development of chemical substances that affect the psychology as well as the physiology of people, in both normal and disturbed states. The education and the training and selection of individuals for work in the world has undergone major changes as the result of what scientists have discovered about learning and human abilities.

Sigmund Freud

Many of the attributes and effects of mental effort must reside in the brain. Everyone has this organ of the human body and, therefore, instinctively feels that he must know something about it. For these reasons, the discovery of mental processes through the study of the brain would seem to be logical and potentially simple. This is very far from being the fact. Observation and experimentation on human brains in health and disease, and analogous experimentation on the brains of animals have during recent years given a large amount of information which previously was unavailable. But there are still many unknowns despite the long and arduous investigations. The exact functions of even large parts of the brain are still mysterious and unsolved.

What is not known about the complexities and wonders of the human brain should not obscure the considerable amount of knowledge that has been acquired over the years. There is extreme complexity in the brain. This can be realized when the experts tell us this living organ, which diverts and controls all of us, consists of neurons, thousands of millions of living nerve cells, additional supporting cells, blood and blood vessels, and other liquids. During intense brain activity connections must be made between the nerve cells that far exceed in number and speed the operation and interconnection of the most advanced so-called electronic brains which are calculating wonders of the age. Experiments during brain operation show that, when the cortex, or outer part,

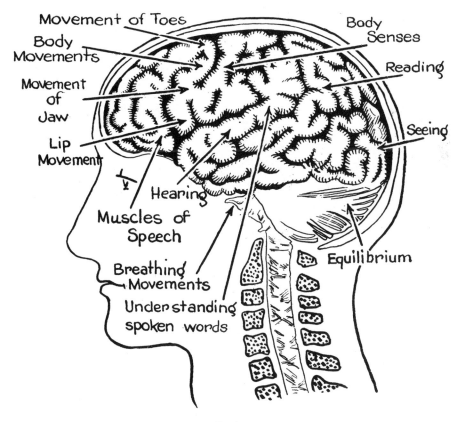

Brain.

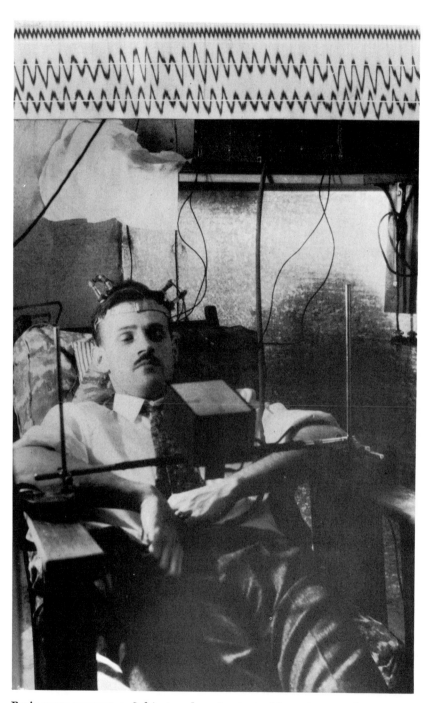

Brain-wave apparatus. Subject undergoing test with equipment of Dr. H. H. Jasper and Dr. L. Carmichael of Brown University, R.I.

of the cerebral hemisphere is stimulated electrically, the patient can recall memories of the past so vividly that he has difficulty realizing he is not experiencing them then. Such experiments suggest that the cortex has laid down successive conscious experience in a relatively permanent pattern of nerve-cell connections. It is as though it were a recording tape that could be replayed in the future. The experiences of a person from childhood onward may be thus recorded upon the cortex. This may be the basis of the wonderful phenomena of memory and recall.

While it has not been determined precisely where the astounding learning ability and memory of human beings reside in their brains, the amount of research and understanding of these factors in human ability is considerable. Learning is not the sole prerogative of the human animal, as shown by the early classic experimental study of dogs by the Russian physiologist, Ivan Pavlov. The "conditioned reflex" which he demonstrated found its way into ordinary language used by those who have only a vague

Dr. John R. Knott, head of the electroencephalography laboratory at the University of Iowa hospital, records the brain waves of John Mattill, graduate student in journalism. Inset shows normal brain-wave records of person first asleep and then awake.

STATE UNIVERSITY OF IOWA

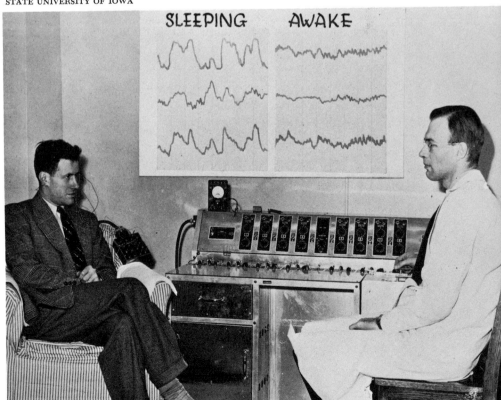

idea of psychology and its details. Pavlov, interested in digestion, and studying gastric secretion and watering of the mouth, found that when dogs were put into situations related to their usually obtaining food, they secreted gastric juices and saliva through glandular reflexes, even if the food were not forthcoming. This gave rise to a whole group of explorations of behavior due to similar conditioning.

The early experiences of animals have been found to exert a profound effect on their behavior when they grow up to maturity. It seems that the earlier the experience, the more influence it has in later life. Experiments with pigeons, chickens, ducks, and guinea pigs, for instance, show that they become attached to the first objects they see. This *imprinting*, as the phenomenon of early social contacts determining adult social behavior is called, can cause a duckling to follow a decoy, or a new-born guinea pig to follow a human being about as though it were its mother. Whether imprinting is important in human infants is an intriguing question.

Emotions, which play a dominating part in relations between human beings, reside in part in a person's memory and experience in the brain, and in part in the bodily functions which are often a "feed-back" to thoughts, feeling, and experience. Emotions are so important that it is little wonder that they are of great concern

Ivan Petrovich Pavlov, noted Soviet scientist, shown upon his return from the London Scientific Congress to take the chair at the Physiological Congress held in Leningrad.

SOVFOTO

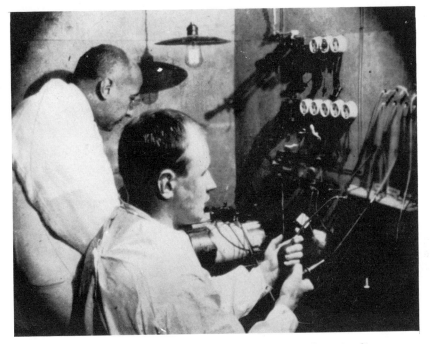

Scientists in Pavlov's laboratory, demonstrating how the stimuli are presented to the dog in Pavlov's experiments.

to those who strive experimentally to understand the functioning of human beings. Such research is equally of concern to those who study and manipulate emotional behavior to control and remedy abnormal behavior.

The research and observation upon both animals and people by psychologists of this century, notably W. B. Cannon and his associates, show that the part of the brain below the cerebral cortex called the hypothalamus plays a key part in emotion. When something arouses a person, messages are transmitted about what is sensed from ears, eyes, or other parts of the body to the nervous system. These react upon the hypothalamus and warn the cortex. Together these dispatching centers put muscles, glands, and other parts of the body into action to react and handle what has been sensed depending on whether it is dangerous or pleasurable to the person. The brain is not alone in reacting to emotions and putting countermeasures into operation. Muscles, intestines, glands, stomach and other parts of the body are involved in the expression of emotions and are linked with what is called the autonomic or

Eighty-six-year-old Soviet physiologist Pavlov and Sir Frederick Banting of Toronto, Canada, discoverer of insulin, meet in Leningrad.

sympathetic nervous system, a complex interplay of cells and other parts of the body. It was found that the two systems within the body, the essentially brain-dominated one and the other controlled by the sympathetic nervous system, are often antagonistic, but sometimes complementary, in their effects. The organs of the body get orders from two headquarters, as it were, and the balance is wonderfully effective in controlling the actions of the body.

Major emotions put the body in an emergency state, ready to meet the threat of danger or the pleasure of experiences ranging from love to eating.

Experience and previous learning greatly affect emotions. Facial expressions which had previously been associated with fear or laughter are likely to bring forth those emotions when seen. Bodily changes caused by emotions can be measured by the rate of oxygen consumption in metabolism, the changes in blood pressure, heart rate, speed of breathing, and even changes in the chemical make-up of blood and urine. A cat that has been frightened by a barking dog has more adrenalin in its blood than one that has not been emotionally aroused in this way.

Many of the patterns of emotion are developed in infancy and childhood, such as crying, laughter, or fighting patterns. When they persist in later years, they are less condoned and understood. When emotional states are uncontrolled and greatly varied, they may be signs of serious mental diseases. Alternation between elation and despondency is characteristic of manic-depressive mental illness, for example.

Emotional states connected with severe mental illness have long been recognized. Almost within the century, disturbed mental states have been recognized as illness rather than as conditions to be corrected by confinement and punishment. The immense problem of mental disease is shown by the fact that the mentally ill occupy over half of the hospital beds of the nation. Major advances in the understanding of the cause and treatment of the major mental illnesses have not been accomplished to the

Dog in Russian laboratory taking part in an experiment to test its power of discrimination.

extent that infectious diseases have been treated chemothera-peutically or antibiotically. Greater understanding of mental states has been achieved and, thanks in part to the tranquilizers and similar pharmacological drugs, handling of mental disease has greatly improved.

In addition to extreme emotional and mental disorder that are disease patterns in themselves, there are effects of deep-seated emotions, fears, frustrations, and other effects upon the physical symptoms of individuals. This psychosomatic medicine, as it is called, not only demonstrates dramatically the relationship be-tween the emotions of patients and their physical symptoms, but it has allowed physicians in many cases to effect psychic treat-ments for disorders which had not been previously recognized as having an emotional basis. Many of the psychosomatic difficulties are due to inappropriate reaction of some organ or part of the body to a situation. When a person prepares to eat a meal, the lining of his stomach becomes engorged with blood, its secretion is greatly increased, and contractions speed up. The same re-actions occur as a consequence of anger or preparing to fight, even if the danger does not happen. If this situation is prolonged, the person will have ulcers. Skin disorders are known to arise under threat of danger because blood vessels and unusual secretions in

Dr. Walter B. Cannon (1871–1945), one of the greatest of U.S. physiologists, first to utilize X-rays in physiological studies.

WILL RAPPORT

Pigeons trained to spot trouble in production line. They peck a warning that discards the defective article.

the skin are inappropriate responses. The kidney may be damaged because it gets too little blood under these circumstances. The heart and blood vessels may overwork as though a fight were confronting the individual, even though he may be quietly inactive and not actually responding otherwise physically to his danger. Such relations between disease and emotional health have constituted one of the most interesting chapters in recent medicine, just as the probing of the subconscious by psychoanalysis has brought about startling and promising remedies and understanding of human actions.

Two groups of scientists have explored and applied the modern knowledge about mind and emotions. The psychologists are mostly interested in normal behavior and the physiological and mental aspects of the brain and its action. Psychiatrists, who are primarily medical practitioners requiring the M.D. degree as part of their training, are primarily concerned with mental abnormality and disturbed behavior. Psychiatry has come of age in this century after a long period during which the mentally ill were considered in the same class with criminals, confined and restrained forcefully and often cruelly.

Out of the clinical strivings to understand the sick in mind, has arisen the modern practice of psychiatry and the elaborate system of mental hospitals and clinics, largely publicly supported, that care for the mentally ill and attempt to understand and restore patients to normal life.

This recognition of the medical aspects of abnormal behavior was a great preliminary step in scientific psychiatry. The understanding and the treatment of severe mental illnesses have not had successes comparable to the use of chemotherapeutic drugs and antibiotics in infectious diseases. Psychiatry has entered what has been called the "pharmacological period," because of the use of tranquilizers in the medication of the symptoms and the control of patients. There is some hope that eventually psychoses can be understood and treated at least as effectively as leprosy and cancer, if not as conclusively as the pneumonias and tuberculosis.

The rise of Freudian psychoanalysis during the century has given new hope and progress in the treatment of many abnormal human actions, particularly those that are not overtly deep-seated and obviously socially troublesome.

The findings and theories of the Viennese doctor, Sigmund Freud, have had an impact upon almost every field of human knowledge. As they have gained greater acceptance they have led to clinical progress and given new hope to those who are mentally disturbed, and their families and friends. More than a mere means of treating mental illness, psychoanalysis provides insight and understanding of the little foibles of human action which become so immensely important in our relationships with ourselves and others. The technical verbiage of psychoanalysis has entered into common speech. Nearly everyone knows of the Freudian implications of slips of the tongue and of the importance that psychoanalysis gives to dreams, both the images at night and the content reported as experience. Hidden unconscious meanings are ferreted out by the skillful understanding of the psychiatrist of what is said by the subject during their one-sided discussions. Almost everybody knows that the libido is the dynamic expression of the sexual instinct, even though he cannot give that definition of it. Similarly, there is glib utilization of the word "ego," a word that hardly needs definition. Also, psychoanalysis sees human beings dominated by the "life instinct" and the "death instinct."

Into our daily thinking has come the idea that we repress some of our desires into our unconscious, and that this is not just mere forgetting, but represents a burying of desires that are in many cases related to sex. In psychoanalysis the "id" is the reservoir of instinctive impulses. And the "ego" is the portion of the human impulses that comes to the surface. The "superego" criticizes the impulses of the id and, less technically, can be thought of as the human conscience.

Dreams are analyzed in psychoanalysis, and Freud considered them as having all the absurdities, delusions, and illusions of psychoses. What the psychoanalyst learns from his probings brings about, in many cases, a modification of mental life that alleviates or even cures some of the illnesses of the mind. Experience shows that dream interpretation in the hands of the skilled practitioner is a key to the conflicts locked deep in the mind, a human mind which Freud compared to an iceberg, six-sevenths of which is submerged beneath the surface.

The fact that man is not master over his own mind, which has been demonstrated through psychoanalysis in the opinion of its practitioners, was considered by Freud one of the three great historic blows to man's pride. The other two were the times when it was demonstrated that the earth is not the center of the universe, and when Darwin's theory of evolution disproved the theory of special creation of man.

Sex is a basic factor in psychoanalysis. Sex develops gradually from the earliest weeks of infancy to adult life, from normal heterosexual life to sex life of marriage. In the early part of childhood it is considered natural that a son, unconsciously, has his mother as a love object and treats his father with hostility. The continuation of this Oedipus complex into later life causes mental difficulties.

Research, discussion, and understanding of sex has grown to be respectable and scientific as the century progressed, partly as a result of psychiatry's bringing to conscious discussion the buried human preoccupation with sex. This psychological and psychiatric understanding of sex and its impact upon ordinary people has been more and more recognized. It has been known more widely to the public than the equally significant understanding of the physiological researches of the reproductive cycle, the whole wonderful exploration of human procreation, and studies of sex ethics and practices.

Much of our understanding of the physiological, psychological, and social aspects of human sex has resulted from the researches conducted under the leadership of the Committee for Research on Problems of Sex of the National Research Council. From this impetus came the discovery of the ovarian hormones, estrogen and progesterone, and the male sex hormones, the androgens. These pharmacological agents not only gave physiological understanding, but, in cases of disorder, powerful control. The research upon reproductive cycles of many animals culminated in precise understanding of the human reproductive cycle and the development of contraceptive materials which makes probable the imminent extension to all populations of safe and simple methods of control. Largely from Japan and Austria, came knowledge, already widely applied, of the so-called "safe-period" of birth control, approximately the last week of the normal twenty-eight-day menstrual cycle.

The famous Kinsey reports on sexual behavior in both the human male and female provided new dimensions for judging sexual behavior and ethics. These and similar inquiries, coupled with the accent upon sex provided by the practice of psychoanalysis and its popularization, brought sex out of the darkness of doctrinaire obscurantism.

The scientific researches upon the human mind and emotions show that man is indeed an animal, but an extraordinary one. He has been able to obtain understanding and insight into his own actions and into the mental and bodily attributes with which he has been endowed by nature. The human race has developed through scientific research and by understanding the means of further progress and control of itself, a prospect which may overshadow other scientific achievements of the century.

HUMAN
TALENT

ONE OF THE GREAT ACHIEVEMENTS of the human race, which differentiates it from other living creatures, is its ability to hand on the experience and knowledge of the past, not genetically but through education. Growing up is the training period in the development and application of human talent. Nurture augments nature.

Education for all as a rightful opportunity came of age with this century. The implementation of equal opportunity for all means "All men are created equal" applied to opportunity rather than precise equality of endowment, as foreseen in the Declaration of Independence. This great and revolutionary philosophical concept fought doggedly for acceptance and reality in the United States, as in the not yet developed areas of the world.

One of the important recognitions in modern times is that, while men should have equality of opportunity, they are not, except in their right to such opportunity, created equal. Their hereditary endowments given them by their biological origins, plus their experience and training in life, markedly affect the quality of performance by individuals. Some children are brighter than others. Some people have great musical talents or quickness in language learning, while others have mathematical and other specialized abilities, not just because they are trained that way, but because there is something in their make-up that gives them these skills and abilities. Recognition of these differ-

265

ences has had an impact on education and the way our schools are organized and taught.

Instead of schooling only for those who are going to become preachers and lawyers, the schools are called upon to prepare people for varied active participation in a growingly complex civilization. The boys and girls are prepared for professions, instead of going to school merely for the purpose of educating them. The growing complexity of civilization created the need for human talent to operate it and to make new discoveries in science and other areas. This potential impact for the future changed the character of the whole structure of education from nursery schools to postgraduate universities.

In the days when education was expanding enormously, it was fashionable to say that we were engaged in a race between intelligence and catastrophe.

Coupled with the potential extension of education to everyone, not just to the end of grammar school but through at least an undergraduate degree in college, has been the revolution in educational methods that has begun to replace didactic rote learning with understanding of the intellectual world, the preparation for democratic living, and service to civilization and self.

John Dewey in a large measure was the innovator and prophet of the twentieth century educational revolution, as Mark Hopkins had been the great personality in nineteenth century education. While Dewey stood for what was called "progressive education" accenting the development of individual abilities, along with the introduction of this freedom in the educational method he insisted upon a rise in the standard of learning. He argued that education should serve the practical needs of society and that individuals should be integrated into the group, at the same time that they were encouraged to develop their full play of interests and abilities.

The kind of education advocated by John Dewey is so much a part of the methods used in mass learning today that it is hard to realize the extent of the intellectual controversy that surrounded him. How applicable in this era of revision of curriculum content are the ideas of Dewey that were so intellectually revolutionary. As an exponent of "learning by doing," Dewey foreshadowed the enmeshing in modern times of both method and content into the enlightened education that has arisen with science and technology. Since the end of World War II there has been a rush attempt to find all of the human talent suitable for the creative discovery of facts and theories, and capable of operating the modern technological civilization. Much of the increase in the ranks of students in our colleges has occurred in scientific and technical schools and courses. A vast array of specialties was born to be added to the old-line areas in engineering, science, medicine, and related fields.

The recrudescence of education in the mode of today began long before it received the scientific impact of World War II with its atom bomb, radar, antibiotics, and dozens of other novelties that became professional necessities. With all this proliferation of higher education, it became increasingly evident that the true age of science began with Galileo and Newton. The direction of education became vital and purposeful when it was realized that knowledge could not be found mainly in the writings and thoughts of the ancients, but had to be obtained from experiments and the questioning and probing of nature itself. Dull memorizing gave way to the venturesome zest of inquiring. Modern education began in earnest.

John Dewey, "progressive educator," emphasized the development of individual abilities and insisted upon rise in the standard of learning.

To the conventional writing, reading, and arithmetic of pioneer days have been added many subjects considered the core of a basic education. Science is one of these, from kindergarten, and even nursery school, through the undergraduate college years. Into some of the liberal courses, such as literature, history, language, and even art, science has crept by force of its impact. The service of science to war and the excitement of man's fling into space gave science more status and time in the nation's schools.

Some science teaching has had a tendency to follow the tradition of English, literature and history, and other "literary" disciplines in being a descriptive subject, learned by reading and listening to lectures rather than by participation. More modern is the return to teaching science as an experimental subject, with laboratories in which the students do experiments themselves, not just watch teachers or read about experiments in books. Instead of being spectators sitting inertly in the science grandstands, the pupils "play science" and learn by swinging at experimental curves and sometimes slamming experimental home-runs. This is in the tradition of the great scientific pioneers of the eighteenth

Dr. B. F. Skinner

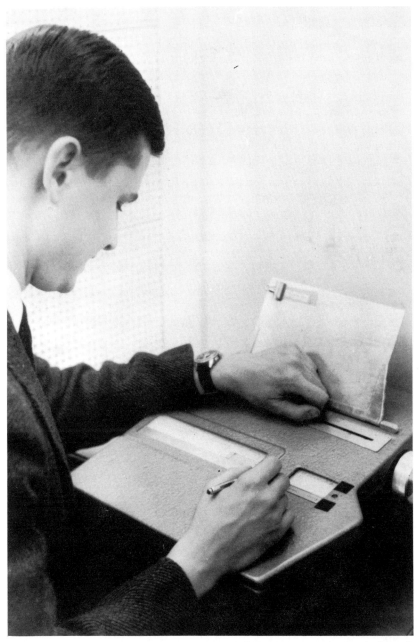

Learning by machine. A student using a Skinner-programmed machine is comparing his answer with a hint of the right answer, given by the machine.

and nineteenth centuries, when telescopes were standard equipment in the libraries of leaders of the times, and when science was the "natural philosophy" which gave birth to the many fields of modern science.

The mass interest of high school students in science as a hobby, as "fun," not compulsion, has created a new educational climate of great promise. Upward of a million boys and girls largely on their own time initiate and complete science projects each year, exhibits of which are shown in science clubs and at science fairs.

America has been fortunate to have escaped the extreme domination of the rigid examinations of Britain and France that irreconcilably determine who shall go on to college.

The greater interest in science and the demands of college entrance have caused a greater variety of science courses to be offered in high schools. There are more "hard" courses in science. General science, that a few decades ago was a beginning high school course, is being pushed into education's earlier years during the upper elementary grades and junior high school.

The conventional secondary school courses in physics, biology, chemistry, and mathematics are undergoing revision by specialized groups of teachers and professors in the hope of speeding and improving the preparation of those who will become the scientists, technologists, and engineers of the future.

Of almost equal importance is the acceptance of science as a part of a "liberal" education for those who will not become specialists—the great bulk of the educated men and women.

At the level of undergraduate and postgraduate education, the specialties have proliferated with the growth of science in research and service to the world. The year is unusual, indeed, that does not see some new highly specialized discipline marked by the awarding of the Ph.D. degree.

In all this, the teacher has won greater appreciation and, incidentally, more salary. Teaching aids of various sorts attempt to reinforce, bolster, and assist the teacher. Some have hoped that TV, LP records, even computers would supplant the live teacher in the classroom, saving tax money. Others have feared that they would. These electronic teacher's helpers have not found their place and are still on trial. Not even in the mechanization of examinations have machines completely taken over, although the "yes or no" and multiple-choice techniques have made some in-

Dr. Robert M. Yerkes, who devised Army Alpha Test.

roads. For language training, tapes are listened to and then compared with the learner's attempts at speaking. This seems to be a successful method.

With the broadening of education in content and in number of students, with the increasing impossibility of a small group of educational peers making judgments of human abilities intuitively and subjectively, professors and administrators turned to more objective and standardized devices of telling which individuals were "brightest," which could best absorb the fruits of education, and which were most effectively learning what was being taught.

Psychologists were called upon to evaluate and test the whole person as well as his academic progress. Tests that could be given to large numbers of individuals were developed as a result of earlier intelligence testing. In the First World War, 1,750,000

Lewis M. Terman

were given the Army Alpha test devised by Dr. Robert M. Yerkes and his associates. In the Second World War, over 10,000,000 drafted men were tested by similar devices. Such tests allowed the classification of men for a large variety of skilled trades and simplified their training.

These successful applications of testing techniques were founded on the concepts of basic intellectual ability and the individual's ability to use abstractions. Just before the twentieth century, the French psychologist, Binet, and his associate, Simon, assembled specific tests and problems that could be given to children of various ages. The scale of more than fifty items and problems were relatively independent of education and were not just information tests. Thus, from these early test applications was developed the idea of mental age. If the child could do more of the tests than his chronological age suggested, then he was considered to have a higher mental age. The famous I.Q., or intelligence quotient, was developed by William Stern, a German psychologist, by dividing the chronological age into the mental age and multiplying by a hundred. Lewis M. Terman of Stanford

University adapted the Binet test to apply to the American scene, and the revised Stanford-Binet test was widely used with relative success. Other adaptations of intelligence measures were made, for instance, the Wechsler-Bellevue intelligence scale.

In the schooling and intricate and all-important gradings that allow children to pass upward through our educational system, the various kinds of tests have become very important. The I.Q. has taken its place alongside the A's, B's, and C's of report card evaluations in determining who shall advance to further opportunities for education. Aptitude tests are considered as important as achievement tests in the process of selection and admission of students to college. They guide the judgment of the educational experts who select those best suited to higher education.

The Science Talent Search, which began in 1942 with its science aptitude test and original experimental project report, was able to aid in the selection of those at the secondary school senior level who are likely to become the creative scientists of the future.

In a large variety of situations, manipulation tests have been devised, starting with the manipulation of geometrically formed blocks by nursery school children. Mechanical aptitude tests were developed for picking those who would make good workers in creative or repetitive tasks in factories. Testing has also been found useful in determining musical and even artistic ability. Testing is necessarily complex and very time-consuming. Careful development of batteries of tests and their standardization must precede their extensive use and the determination of the reliance to be placed upon them.

Aptitude and intelligence tests do not tell the whole story of the usefulness of the individual and whether he will fit into our civilization. Personality and character, more difficult to measure than intelligence, play an equally important role. Often the roles of the psychologist and psychiatrist merge in a study of human personality and character. Much can be determined from the reactions of individuals to manufactured or real situations and from their past history. Opinions of the people who know the person being evaluated are useful in determining loyalty, honesty, courage and "stick-to-itiveness." Whether a person is emotionally stable or unstable, whether he has a sense of humor, and whether he likes people or he lives largely within himself are important in assaying personality, character, and fitness. These attributes are important in judging whether a person fits into a position or a social situation.

Personality tests have been developed. One of these is the so-called Rorschach test named after the European psychiatrist who developed it. The person being tested for personality looks at ten standard ink blots and tells what pictures and meaning he sees in them. This play of imagination to suggestion gives clues to drives, wishes, and social status. The results, when meas-

On the opposite page are sample questions from the two-hour Science Aptitude Examination taken by high-school seniors in the Twenty-second Annual Science Talent Search. If you don't know all the answers, take comfort. The test is deliberately designed to screen out all but the best among thousands of very able students. None has made a perfect score in the entire twenty-two years of the Science Talent Search.

Dr. Harold A. Edgerton, Washington psychologist, constructed the Twenty-second Science Aptitude Examination. He also is chairman of the Science Talent Search judging committee.

As one of the measuring devices of the Search, it is designed to test ability to think and reason in terms of scientific concepts and vocabulary. Most science-minded high school seniors find the examination challenging and enjoyable to take since it is much like the problems, puzzles, and games so many of them delight in solving.

Scores on this test represent only one part in the judging procedures that select the students who seem most likely to become outstanding research scientists. There is no predetermined "passing" grade.

Detailed scholastic records of each "passing" contestant were evaluated. Information offered by the student and his faculty sponsor about his accomplishments, activities, traits, and attitudes was weighed carefully to find any of a number of good combinations of achievement and promise.

Each entrant was required to submit a written report of an individual research project, usually about a thousand words of text, plus relevant diagrams, graphs, theorems, pictures, etc.

The papers of all the students were read critically by a board of professional scientists, which included specialists in the many fields explored by the student-scientists. This board studied and evaluated reports on computer methods, viruses, planet observations, lasers, complex mathematics, microorganisms, and more than a thousand other subjects.

In the Twenty-second Science Talent Search, 22,477 sets of examination materials were requested. There were 3,274 completely qualified entries judged, and 40 top winners.

The five scholarships of $7,500, $6,000, $5,000, $4,000 and $3,000, and the thirty-five awards of $250 each may be used at any accredited college or university and are intended to assure the professional training of these young pre-scientists.

PART A

DIRECTIONS: Four possible answers are given for each question. Choose that one answer which is *most nearly correct*.

1. The best fuel for use in present fuel cells is
   1. carbon
   2. hydrogen
   3. kerosene
   4. sodium

2. The term "systolic" would probably be found in an article on
   1. abstract mathematics
   2. heart research
   3. plastics
   4. soil conservation

3. A klystron is most closely related to a
   1. bevatron
   2. mho
   3. mitochondria
   4. vacuum tube

10. Which of the following causes hyperopia?
    1. increased fluid pressure on the eye
    2. lengthened focal length of eye lens
    3. shortened focal length of eye lens
    4. uneven curvature of the cornea

11. An anthropologist believes that the first man from outer space to be seen by earth men will be bimanous, quadrupedal hexapods. Such outer space men will
    1. have four limbs
    2. have six feet
    3. have two hands
    4. not be bilaterally symmetrical

12. Pyroclastic cones are
    1. for measuring subterranean pressure
    2. for measuring temperature
    3. rocket nose cones
    4. cones of volcanic ejecta

13. The Milky Way Galaxy, to which the earth and sun belong is a huge
    1. concave disc
    2. diffuse globule
    3. doughnut-shaped pattern
    4. spiral with three arms

PART B

SECTION D

The differential chain block, shown in the diagram, consists of two sheaves, A and B, A being double sheave having diameters R and r. The multiplying power of this mechanism depends upon the ratio of these diameters. If they are equal, the pull P will not move the weight, and the efficiency of the mechanism will be zero percent, but the theoretical mechanical advantage is infinity. A slight difference in radii will produce a very large lifting effort, although the efficiency may still be very low. The sheaves are made with link pockets so that the chain fits nicely into the circumference, and is restrained from slipping. Furthermore, the chain is endless, and the mechanism is self-locking by virtue of the friction intentionally allowed on the journals.

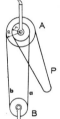

In explanation of the chain block, if the pull P revolves sheave A one revolution, the vertical chain at a is lowered through a distance to $2\pi r$, while the side b is raised the distance $2\pi R$. The net vertical displacement of the sheave B is $\pi(R-r)$ upward. With no friction considered, the the work of lifting W through this distance must be equal to the work done by the pull P moving through $2\pi R$. Solving this equation for advantage $\frac{W}{P}$,

$$\frac{W}{P} = \frac{2R}{R-r}.$$

Applying the mechanical efficiency e to this equation, the actual mechanical advantage is

$$\frac{W}{P} = \frac{2\,Re}{R-r}$$

These chain blocks are built in different sizes for hoisting loads from one-quarter ton to three or four tons, by hand. On account of the self-locking feature depending on friction, the average mechanical efficiency of this device is only about 30%.

QUESTIONS ON SECTION D

38. Which of the following statements is true? When the pull P revolves sheave A two revolutions, and sheaves A and B have the same diameter, then
    1. if R = r, sheave B can only rotate in place
    2. if R > r, sheave B will be lowered
    3. if R < r, sheave B will be raised
    4. for any values of R and r, sheave B will be neither lowered nor raised

39. The multiplying power of the mechanism is
    1. a function of the ratio of R and r
    2. limited by the amount of pull a man can exert
    3. lowered by the amount of friction present
    4. the same as the mechanical advantage

40. As sheave B is raised through the use of the mechanism
    1. the chain loop of P will become larger
    2. the chain loop of P will become smaller
    3. the chain loop of P will remain the same size
    4. no information is available to show relationship of length of the chain loop of P and travel of sheave B

41. If R = 10 inches and r = 8 inches, how much will sheave B be raised by 10 complete revolutions of sheave A?
    1. 8π inches
    2. 18π inches
    3. 20π inches
    4. 25π inches

42. Using the equation for mechanical advantage given, and assuming that mechanical efficiency is 40%, what is the advantage of a differential chain block in which the diameters of the double sheave are 20 and 15, and the diameter of sheave B is 10?
    1. 2.4
    2. 2.8
    3. 3.2
    4. 3.6

PART C

DIRECTIONS: READ these directions carefully. Each question has four possible answers, BUT there may be as many as FOUR right answers for a question. For some questions there will be only one right answer, while others may have two, three or four right answers.

77. The earth has two natural, cloud-like satellites. Which of the following statements about this phenomenon are true?
    1. They are part of the Van Allen belt.
    2. They are presumably a swarm of tiny particles or meteors.
    3. They follow about the same path as does the moon relative to the earth.
    4. They travel in nearly circular paths around the earth.

79. Niobium is
    1. a metal
    2. an element
    3. an opiate
    4. a rare earth

80. Which of the following have been found to be parts of one or another bacterial cell?
    1. a nucleus
    2. centrosome
    3. slime layer
    4. sulfur particles

81. A star's color indicates its temperature. In this case
    1. blue giant stars are hottest
    2. dimmest stars are farthest away
    3. red stars are the coolest
    4. yellow stars are hottest

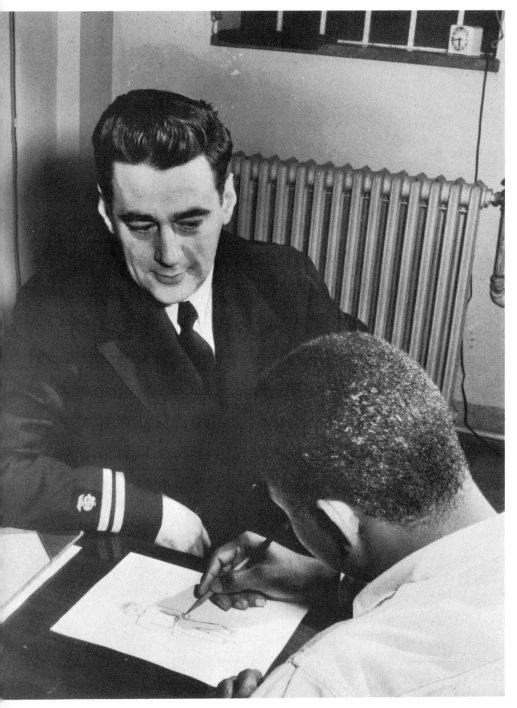

Mental tests.

ured against standardized responses, give some idea of basic interests and attitudes.

There are other tests like the Rorschach—such as the thematic apperception test, TAT, based on a series of pictures that are interpreted by the person being tested. In a play of fancy and in reactions to the situations presented, character and personality are likely to be revealed.

Physique and bodily functioning affect personality, character, and even intelligence. Ancients attributed the power of personality effects to so-called *humors* in our body, bile for instance being linked to a melancholy disposition and phlegm to phlegmatic temperament. The old conceptions have been disproved, but internal secretions and hormones do have great influence upon the personality and character.

The size, appearance, and physique of an individual affect personality and character in the way that other people receive and treat him.

The many complexities of human talent have received extraordinary exploration and understanding since the turn of the century. Yet, there is more to be learned. From the research that combines psychology, psychiatry, physiology, a host of medical fields, and education will come continued guidance to the complex interplay of people with all aspects of life in many situations.

RESEARCH, THE GREAT INVENTION

THE GREATEST INVENTION in the history of mankind was the scientific, or research, process. This consists of making observations of what happens in nature or, when some situation is created, determining what general rule may apply, then testing and retesting the hypothesis until it can be safely assumed true. In contrast to the dogmatism of the long expanse of human history until about the middle of the eighteenth century, this scientific or research method of arriving at truth and doing things is relatively recent in the history of the world. Although it is essential to the whole rise of scientific discovery and application, this new way of thinking came in with the scientific renaissance led by Galileo, Newton, and the other great greats.

The dogmatism of religion, with its insistence upon revealed and fixed truth, hampered the growth of the scientific method of arriving at truth and fact, but it could not bar its eventual progress.

The power of example and the demonstration of methods of thinking speeded the growth of scientific exploration and the finding of principles and laws that would tell what could be expected to happen reliably. The idea grew that nature behaved in a regular way. Quite as important as the prediction of what would happen was the use of principles to tell what would not happen. The future could be predicted.

Nature's actions could be foreseen. Man could design novel

278

devices and tell how they were going to work. The nature of things became understandable, controllable, and, above all, predictable with assurance. The great intellects, that perceived the new view of the world and utilized the new methods which is science, began to recreate and change our environment as well as our thinking.

Great advances in science and technology of the century have been made by organized teams working in research laboratories, under commercial, educational, or governmental control and support. The lone-wolf inventor, the man in the garret, began to go out of fashion with the turn of the century. Innovation and invention continued to be accomplished by brilliant individuals, but the process of exploration was greatly accelerated and aided by the interplay of many disciplines and minds. With the increasing complexity of the advance of knowledge and the inability of any one expert to master the details of even a single field, the group method of inquiry became more necessary.

Just as Galileo, Copernicus, Newton, Darwin, Pasteur, and Mendel were able to make epochal formulations and discoveries in relative isolation, so, in more recent decades, individuals like Einstein, Baekeland, De Forest, Land, and a host of others made great inventions and discoveries essentially on their own.

A twentieth century development was the great research laboratory, with groups of researchers, supported by industrial or governmental funds, which relieved the individual scientist from worry about his financial support and the management of the property of his creation. Research became organized "big business" either in the interests of corporations or of the public through government.

The foremost example of American inventive ingenuity, Thomas A. Edison, was the originator of industrial research which became so important in the discovery, invention, and application of useful processes and products. Edison, himself, in his West Orange, New Jersey, Laboratory had a large number of assistants, working as he told them to do upon an investigation in which he was engaged. These did not constitute a contributing and participating team effort exactly like present research groups. But the Edison technique did bring more hands and more brains to bear on a single problem.

Edison's electrical discoveries gave rise to the General Electric

Original home of General Electric Research Laboratory (1900) in barn behind home of C. P. Steinmetz.

Company. It was no mere accident that this company's laboratory was the first in American industry to engage in scientific research for its own sake, rather than merely for the development of some product or device that could be foreseen. Until this century no laboratory of this sort had existed. Scientists, engineers, and laboratory technicians were given the opportunity of spending time and money on experiments that were not sure to turn out successfully.

With the demonstration of this successful technique of discovery and development, research laboratories multiplied throughout

America and the world as the century grew older. DuPont became the first company in the chemical field to do organized chemical research. Beginning with explosives during the American Revolution, DuPont now is in almost every field of chemical and physical inquiry, continuing to create many new products, such as nylon, dacron, synthetic rubber, etc. Bell Telephone Laboratories became one of the largest research establishments, initially devoted to the improvement of telephone devices, but later to the development of transistors, television, computing methods, and other modern essentials.

The great pharmaceutical concerns have created in their laboratories new drugs for the cure and prevention of disease, largely as the result of new biophysical, biochemical, and medical science research, in most cases not directed precisely at the disease that has been affected by the new drug. Industries in every field have laboratories, and must have them, in order to keep up with the swiftly moving pace of new products and new demands. In many cases research brings about the first diversification for industry because what is found in the laboratories leads the company into activities it had not engaged in traditionally. The largest industrial corporations of the nation, with very few exceptions, are those which have strong and well-supported research laboratories. In the latest listing of industrial research laboratories there are 4,145 organizations of various sorts.

In addition to laboratories operated by industries, research institutes both for profit and nonprofit are located in strategic parts of the United States. This American development allows the conduct of research on specific problems without the need for an industry to establish extensive special laboratories.

The first of these research institutes that set the pattern was the Mellon Institute at Pittsburgh, at which associations of manufacturers maintain industrial fellowships. Notable among the other research institutes of the nation are Battelle Memorial Institute, Columbus, Ohio, the Stanford Research Institute in California, Midwest Research Institute in Kansas City, Southwest Research Institute in San Antonio, and Southern Research Institute in Birmingham, Alabama. A. D. Little in Cambridge, Massachusetts, performs a similar function, carrying on research and development on its own account and for individual industrial concerns. In some cases trade associations, themselves, have set up their own laboratories. Some universities and engineering colleges have developed industrial research on behalf of associations or groups of manufacturers and individual companies.

The two World Wars demonstrated the power of scientific research in fashioning new weapons for war and military defense. The extensive military expenditures of the nation, utilizing one out of every two tax dollars, provide research and development dollars. Defense efforts have given support on a very large scale to scientific inquiry and research in universities, research institutes, and other organizations. The Department of Defense provides funds for scientific research upon a far greater scale than any other source in the nation, outdistancing both industry and the private foundations which, over the years, sustained research and gave it useful direction at a time when it was most needed. Notably the Carnegie Corporation, the Rockefeller Foundation, and later the Ford Foundation, gave such support and guidance.

The rapidly expanding universities of America are also the centers of research largely supported by federal government funds. Some research continues to be done as adjunct to teaching, particularly at the post-graduate level, but increasingly after World War II the financial sinews for the acquisition of new knowledge in fields of physical, chemical, biological, mathematical, and medical sciences have been the Department of Defense and its various activities, the National Institutes of Health, and the National Science Foundation. Many of the larger universities have reinforced their specialized departments with research activities which are in some cases relatively independent of the actual teaching although usually related to it. Important research organizations have budded from some of the larger universities and have their own independent existence, often on or near the campuses, with the library facilities and the presence of experts from other disciplines that become so necessary in the conduct of fruitful investigations.

The most extensive and the best-implemented medical research effort is contained in the seven National Institutes of Health at Bethesda, Maryland, part of the U.S. Public Health Service of the Department of Health, Education, and Welfare of the federal government. Every field of medical research is covered, and thousands of skillful and well-trained investigators are employed. But the research power of this group is not confined to this

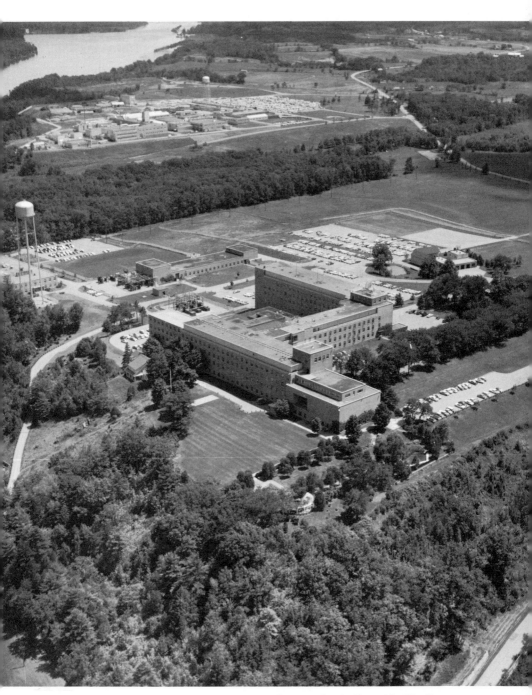

General Electric Research Laboratory in Schenectady, N.Y., with Knolls Atomic Power Laboratory (AEC-GE) in background.

physical institution located at Bethesda. The specialists of the Institutes, reinforced by the judgment of outside experts, award thousands of grants that make medical research possible in medical schools, other universities, and research institutions of various sorts, not only in the United States, but throughout the world. These grant-supported studies, which have been operating only since mid-century, have already produced important results, but the effect of what is learned will bring benefits during the coming decades.

The armed forces, with their own extensive investigational activities, are major performers and supporters of both pure and applied research. The Navy particularly has extensive research laboratories, such as the Naval Research Laboratory and the Naval Ordnance Laboratory, which are the two principal installations near Washington. The research branch of the Navy, the Office of Naval Research, was a pioneer supporter of research through grants. In the days before the establishment of the National Science Foundation, it made available funds to universities and other organizations at a critical time. The Army, Air Force, and Navy have numerous specialized laboratories throughout the country and, again, much of the research that is undertaken is supplemented by projects implemented in universities and colleges. To an extraordinary extent, aeronautics was created in the fundamental researches of the National Advisory Committee for Aeronautics, which was organized during World War I as an independent governmental agency. Government funds established aeronautical research facilities which were responsible for the increasing efficiency and effectiveness of most military and commercial aircraft. Merged with other federal space and astronautical research activities, such as the National Aeronautics and Space Administration, these laboratories, thus augmented by other military and industrial facilities, constitute America's research fling into space.

Some of the most significant research has been conducted in the old-line civilian departments. The National Bureau of Standards was created not long after the turn of the century to assure correct weights and measures for the nation, and to make sure that the government got its money's worth in its extensive purchases. In engineering, physics, chemistry, and mathematics, it has become a powerful research organization. Similarly, the new and better methods of weather prediction have been developed in the U.S. Weather Bureau. The Bureau of Mines, the Geological Survey, and the research activities of the Smithsonian Institution have made significant contributions through the years.

In agriculture and its related sciences, the U.S. Department of Agriculture, with its own laboratories and experimental farms, now at Beltsville, Maryland, and in cooperation with agricultural experimental stations in every state, has been a powerful research agency which has served agriculture and many other sectors of the nation's economy. The agricultural experimental stations are usually parts of the great land grant colleges that are such an important factor in higher education. The creation of new agricultural crops, breeding of superior livestock and poultry, the fight against insects and plant diseases, the development of new uses for farm products, and many other aids to scientific agriculture have resulted from this sustained and well supported program.

The whole world has been the beneficiary of American research, as discoveries and investigations in other parts of the world have been usefully transplanted to America. In the first decade of this century, Germany, with its universities and developing industrial laboratories, was the training ground for American scientists. The First World War demonstrated how dependent the United States was upon German chemical knowledge and manufacturing, particularly of dyes and pharmaceuticals. There was an awakening to the necessity for American chemical production and the need of basic and thorough teaching of science in our colleges, coupled with support for research and graduate Ph.D. study. Seizure of German patents and utilization of the resulting royalties through the Chemical Foundation awoke people to the necessity of chemical independence from Europe, and stimulated scientific education and industry in this country.

The two great wars caused the creation of research organizations to meet the military emergencies, just as the National Academy of Sciences, the elite science organization in America and counterpart of Britain's Royal Society, had been created by Act of Congress during the Civil War. The National Research Council was organized under the National Academy of Sciences during World War I and still continues as a major co-ordinating body for American scientific societies and organizations. The

Office of Scientific Research and Development and its predecessor, the National Science Defense Committee, were the research agencies for military purposes during World War II. While these were not perpetuated as such, out of the war research effort came the plans and recommendations which resulted in the creation of the National Science Foundation in 1950, as a government agency for planning and for giving grants in various fields, but not as an organization that runs its own laboratories.

Great Britain has had a scientific research development which is parallel to that of the United States, sufficiently compatible with the American effort to allow fruitful co-operation on war projects during World War II. Almost every industrially advanced country, since the time of World War I, has supported and stimulated research through organizations similar to those in Great Britain and the United States.

The amount of money invested in research and development has risen prodigiously in this century. This is not surprising, considering the fruitfulness of such expenditures in terms of military protection, betterment of everyday life, and devices out of which industry can make a profit.

The federal government's appropriations for the support of scientific research and development reached the level of $10,800,-000,000 for the fiscal year ending June 30, 1962. This can be compared with less than $75,000,000 in 1940.

Most of the large increase is due to defense activities. In the fiscal year 1962, three agencies—the Department of Defense, the Atomic Energy Commission, and the National Aeronautics and Space Administration—obligated an estimated 90 per cent of the federal scientific and development budget, the Department of Defense accounting for $6,200,000,000 alone.

While the exact amount of expenditures for research and development activities on the part of corporations is difficult to estimate, they increased as the century grew older. Corporation-conducted research did not have the defense stimulation from industry itself, although in many cases great corporations, skilled in research techniques were conducting research and development on behalf of the defense branches of the government with federal funds.

As the century's sixth decade began, the total research and development of the nation was estimated as upward of twelve

Scientific maze: Six hundred glass fittings and approximately five miles of piping in the new Developmental Research Center of CIBA Pharmaceutical Company. Underneath the new research center there are three hundred feet of glass sewer lines.

Hughes Aircraft Company's Research Laboratories at Malibu, Calif.

billion dollars. Research expenditures were four times what they were just ten years earlier. Some estimates place the probable annual research outlay in 1970 at from twenty billion to twenty-five billion dollars.

Expenditures for research and development reached over 2 per cent of the gross national product (GNP) during the later years of the 1950's, amounting to 2.6 per cent in 1959.

It is important to differentiate between expenditure for development and for research. Included in the figures given are expenditures for experimental work which includes such things as reactors, missiles, and a host of other developments of "hardware," mechanisms useful in the defense effort. For basic or "pure" research, the kind of untrammeled investigations that are more likely to produce new knowledge, the federal government in its peak year spent about one dollar out of each ten used for research and development, excluding expenditures for the physical plant in which research and development were conducted. This is the very considerable sum of $850,000,000. The federal funds for basic research are 44 per cent allocated to educational institutions, 30 per cent to federal agencies, 14 per cent to profit organizations, and 12 per cent to other agencies. Somewhat over half of the basic research funds are devoted to the physical sciences, including mathematics and engineering, a little over a quarter to the life sciences, and the rest among psychological, social, and other sciences.

The inquiry into scientific problems without primary consideration of so-called "practical" results is the life blood of scientific, medical, industrial, and even national progress. From such basic or "pure" research come the great new developments, the "breakthroughs" which change the course of living for the whole world. For example, the fission of uranium discovered in a German laboratory under Hitler's unseeing eyes was the beginning of the whole atomic energy development. The discoverers had no idea that they were making possible the atomic bomb. Exploration and investigation, motivated simply by the desire to know, are the most powerful factors in scientific progress.

Those who conduct research and make it possible for others to do so are by no means agreed on just what basic research is and how "pure" it must be. Some will argue for the usefulness of useless knowledge, and history bears them out most emphatically.

Others will point to fruitful results from investigations which know fairly well where they are going and are analogous to the kind of risk that oil companies take when they drill wells upon the advice of geologists. One suggestion as to the employment of the term *basic* is that it should be applicable to work done solely at the inclination of the investigator, that it does not have to be done, and that it is not immediately or even eventually in the interests of anybody else. This kind of research is most frequently done in university laboratories or research organizations which are themselves created with a conviction that anything additional that is known will be of some worth to the progress of the world. As an example, in the wide research attack on cancer, perhaps the century's most well-supported fundamental attack upon any problem the solution of which is not evident, there are investigators engaged on many lines of inquiry far removed from anyone ill with the disease.

Louis Pasteur observed that there were not two forms of science, pure and applied, but only science and the application of science. Charles F. Kettering characteristically commented that to have a direction and inspiration for research is useful, that a man is more likely to stumble over things if he is trying to go somewhere than if he is sitting still. The somewhat pompous word *serendipity* means the same thing. The impractical scientist who explores widely may be the most practical in terms of results obtained. If the dreamer is also a doer, his dreams may indeed come true. The more people there are who get ideas and try them out in the light of what has been discovered before, the faster science and technology will advance.

Freedom in scientific research ranks in importance as a fundamental democratic tenet with personal liberty, freedom of speech and press, and religious liberty, guaranteed by the Constitution of the United States. Education has become an inalienable right, necessary for every developing child. For the public good as well as the individual's benefit, each person should, and does in America, have the privilege of developing his talents according to his best judgment and desires. This system, under freedom, has operated to produce a balanced labor and professional human force of extraordinary variety and effectiveness.

Freedom to search for new knowledge is an important facet of this intellectual liberty. Implicit in the scientific method is

NATIONAL INSTITUTES OF HEALTH

Aerial view of the National Institutes of Health, chief research center of the Public Health Service.

need for the rise of new ideas and their exploration. Most precious are the brains that have the ability to create, to look at things differently, and to dare to differ with existing knowledge. Geniuses and innovators have succeeded often in the past by overcoming obstacles put in their path by tradition and by insistence upon so-called practical results. Science, like other cultural activities, has had to cast off bonds that fettered it.

A realization of the value of untrammeled investigation gives a considerable number of proved specialists the chance to do research where their ideas and findings lead them.

In universities, governmental and industrial research establishments, and individual laboratories, these frontiersmen of knowledge are pushing onward. In some instances, wise foundations have virtually endowed a scientist, assuring him support for the rest of his life by some means or other, confident that the odds favor that his intellectual production will be important. Similarly, scholarships and fellowships are the ways universities, industries, and government bet on the future fruitfulness of promising scientific talent.

The way of scientific investigation is not too rigid and ritualistic. There is ample room for guesses, hunches, and even informed day-dreaming. The formulation of a hypothesis, something to be tested, is essential, and controlled experiment must be analyzed and evaluated with a supreme disregard for preconceived ideas, no matter how emotionally appealing.

When dominated by a philosophical or political speculative predetermination, inquiry will remain stillborn. Research worthy of the term cannot be expected to prove a preconceived notion, only to test it, no matter how authoritatively conceived the philosophy or idea. Philosophies or ideas enunciated with wide acceptance, high prestige, and great authority must bow before crucial experimental trials and tests. For that is science's way of arriving at truth.

The world has more scientists that it ever had before, yet an increasing supply of well-trained and well-motivated scientists and engineers and technologists is required for the future. Doubling and redoubling science's manpower in the next generation seems to be necessary to maintain the fundamental progress of the nation through innovation and new knowledge.

The Soviet success in Sputniks and rocketry, and a look at

Aerial view of the Beltsville Agriculture Research Center and some other buildings.

Russian education, shocked and sensitized America, stimulating the country to give greater attention to the production of scientific and technological manpower. A bolstering of science education was already in progress but Soviet success accelerated it. There is a science rush in our colleges and universities which promises to continue into the future, with the result that there will be enough personnel to maintain research and development as well as operation of the increasingly more technical industrial plant.

The best estimate of the total number of professional scientists and engineers of the nation in all fields is between 1,150,000 and 1,200,000. Of these more than 300,000 are scientists and 800,000 to 850,000 are engineers. One may add to these figures the physicians of the nation, less than 250,000, not including scientists involved in medical research.

During the depression of the 1930's, when some of those who were technically trained had difficulty finding jobs, a government department was sufficiently pessimistic to predict that there would be too many engineers in the future. A few years later this same government department was concerned with trying to find a sufficient number of engineers and to encourage the training of additional ones. The pace of technical development and the use of all persons with scientific and technical training give promise of continuing acceleration. The future will unquestionably see spirited bidding for the services of scientists and engineers.

Patents are often the culmination of the ingenuity of both organized teams of investigators in research laboratories and independent inventors. The increase in the number of U.S. patents issued during the century is an index of technological progress. Over four times as many patents were issued during the first six decades of the century than were granted during the preceding years from the beginning of the patent system in 1790. Patent No. 686,046 was given on November 5, 1901, to Henry Ford for "new and useful improvements in motor carriages." Patent No. 1,000,000 was issued in 1911, No. 2,000,000 in 1935, No. 2,500,000 in 1950, and No. 3,000,000 in 1961.

Patents give a legal monopoly to the inventor for 17 years which is about the minimum span of human generations. It is not very much longer than the time that it takes to get a new idea adopted or a new device into production and distribution.

Under the stress of war and with the expenditure of over a billion dollars, the discovery of uranium fission was developed into an atomic bomb exploded in war in the short period of 6½ years. This is a relatively short time. The period of gestation of an invention or a new discovery is usually much longer. The time lag of accomplishment in most cases is certainly a decade or more. When it is realized that it takes several years to publish and circulate new scientific discoveries even before their utilization and development begins, it is evident that we are now receiving the benefit of what happened in laboratories at least a decade and a half ago, and that each year's scientific researches are nourishing the relatively distant future.

The time-lag in the realization of the power of research itself is even longer, for the idea and the technique of the investigational method that is called research is not a twentieth century invention, no matter how powerful it has been in this century. Fortunately, as for an expired patented invention, there is no monopoly on the research idea. What has been accomplished by research is available for the whole world, and what will be discovered in coming years gives promise for the future.

THE
ENTICING
FUTURE

THE IDEA OF CONTINUED PROGRESS is the prime scientific fact that underlies the research and investigation approach. It is the very essence of our science. If we do not go forward, we stagnate. The animal that does not evolve slowly but surely runs a great risk of becoming extinct as the dinosaur. Our future is necessarily unfinished, and if we did not expect things to change there would be no use going on doing the things we are doing.

Many lines of progress in the future can be foreseen and predicted. The accomplishment of some of these will need the concentration of brains and energy, and the expenditure of billions, that characterized the atomic energy program during World War II. Some other future possibilities can be materialized for less money, but will require motivation and desire that may be difficult to achieve.

Some of the most needed and most difficult problems of science need solution. Let us outline some of them.

We need to use the sun's energy more effectively.

For its bulk sources of energy, our civilization is dependent upon fossil sunshine. Coal, oil, and natural gas are the sunshine of past geological ages. We of this century are spending them profligately. Most of our food and a small part of our energy, in the form of wood and water power, is energized with relatively current sunshine. The earth would be dead and lifeless without

296

the atomic radiations from the sun, eight minutes of light-travel time away from earth.

The achievement of capturing the sun's energy in a useful way and on a large scale without the intervention of the green leaf and its process of photosynthesis is one of the great problems of the future. If it could be reached, it would far excel in historical importance the release of atomic energy and its far-reaching effects.

Only a relatively small amount of research is going into this problem of artificial photosynthesis. Perhaps a dozen laboratories are intensively at work upon the problem.

Success may come through the discovery of a method of economically capturing the sun's energy through some chemical reaction which is not the same as that used by the green plant. Or, it may be possible to discover the seemingly complex mechanism of chemical transformations used in natural photosynthesis, and then to duplicate and simplify it for industrial utilization.

Artificial photosynthesis may very well be only a few billions of dollars and a few years away if people and government could be convinced of its real importance.

Power from atomic fusion should be achieved. The raw material of atomic energy today is primarily uranium, a very rare element indeed, and possibly thorium. For a decade or two it has been suspected that the sun and the stars stoke themselves with a much more plentiful element, hydrogen, which is at the other end of the atomic scale. The hydrogen bomb was achieved almost simultaneously by the United States and Soviet Russia. It converts the mass of hydrogen in the form of its twin and triplet elements, deuterium and tritium, into energy. There seems to be some chance that it will be possible to have quiet and controlled hydrogen-isotope fusion so that atomic power, conversion of mass into energy, can be achieved from the lightest of the elements.

If this can be done, and we are not sure that it can be, it will be an achievement far greater than that of the fission of uranium which ushered in the present atomic era. It could bring an industrial benefit of great social significance out of the hydrogen bomb development.

Better understanding of nuclear forces is needed.

The part of the universe lying within the atom is most mysterious and relatively unexplored. Among the protons, the neutrons, and the other subatomic particles, the laws which govern larger objects with which we are familiar do not seem to hold. One of the problems ahead is to understand these forces within the nucleus. Study of cosmic rays is primarily aimed at this problem, since they are created in the outside universe beyond the earth and smash into our atmosphere with tremendous energies, capable of destroying the atomic structures which we find impregnable even in our largest atomic accelerators. There is a full realization of the importance of this problem. That is why giant atom smashers, the cyclotrons, the synchrotrons, and the linear accelerators, are being built with large expenditures of money as an adjunct to our atomic energy program. Scientists do not know exactly what will be discovered, but they are sure that important new knowledge will come from within the atom.

We are not sure that we know the nature of the universe.

This earth upon which we live is a relatively average planet of a rather insignificant star, one of millions upon millions of stars in millions upon millions of galaxies or island universes. We know much more about the universe in which we live than we did two or three decades ago, thanks to big and wide-eyed telescopes. The size of the universe has been doubled over what it was thought to be, according to the latest astronomical researches. And radio waves from outer space are another kind of radiation, besides light and heat, that signal the universe's extent and let us observe the presence of bodies that do not shine, during clear or cloudy weather, day or night.

Philosophically and practically from the standpoint of human intelligence, we must know what our universe is and what we are in it. That is the task of astronomers who feed their facts to philosophers, which most of us imagine we are.

Certainly the nature of the universe is one of our great and continuing problems which may take many more centuries, if ever, to solve completely. In the heavens experiments of immense time and size are in progress. Whence did we come? Where are we going? How old is the universe? The light of constantly renewed stars brings us assurance that atomic energy on a grand scale is being used in other parts of the universe.

Escape from the earth is a future problem.

Comic strips and science fiction have had visitors from other planets coming to earth, and any young TV watcher will be surprised to know that space travel and escape from the earth by rocket ship are considered future problems of science. Our imaginations can solve so many more problems than our aeronautical engineers.

The real frontier of aeronautics is in the supersonic and hypersonic regions where missiles and planes travel beyond the speed of sound (Mach 1). It will be a considerable length of time before there is practical flight at Mach 5 (3,300 miles per hour at high altitude) or beyond, which is known as the hypersonic region. Nevertheless, we have made significant progress in escape by rocket to the space beyond the firm grasp of the earth's gravitation. There are now artificial moons for the earth, satellites which circle around once they are put in their orbits. More astronauts are in training to take to space. Rockets and jet craft are being built to reach any part of the earth from any other part so that no area will be free from the danger of atomic attack. They can travel not only into the outer regions of the earth's gaseous envelope, but to the distant parts of the solar system. The dreams of Jules Verne and his many followers are proving to be not sufficiently daring simply because we cannot escape traveling in the direction that aeronautical technology is taking us.

As a consequence of aeronautical progress, atomic energy, and the need for new engineering materials as operating temperatures are pushed upward, there is greater need for unusual elements such as titanium, zirconium, and many other metals and elements which are less known. Some little-known elements are unavailable except as by-products of the fission of uranium. We seem to have gone about as far as we can in the discovery of elements, although eventually more than the known 103 will be artificially created in minute quantities and without any seemingly useful application. Many of the elements which have been discovered in the last decade are continually exploding themselves to pieces by their radioactivity. The discovery of atomic varieties, or isotopes, in very large numbers has been one of the great chemical achievements.

The menace of radiation is real. Beginning with the discovery of X-rays and radioactivity before the turn of the century, there has been more and more radiation in the world. The advent of the atomic bomb and the use of a wide variety of radioactive isotopes in research and industry make the dangers of radiation more imminent and real.

Radiation has a powerful effect on living matter, whether it be through X-rays and gamma rays (of the same family as light, only shorter in wavelength), or actual particles such as the streams of electrons (beta rays) and helium atomic hearts (alpha rays). Of greatest concern to the human population of the world is the fact that radiation can affect a stream of life carried through the germ cells. Radiation has not been with us in sufficient quantity long enough to make us certain that long-term effects are not being felt by human or other animal life, even from the relatively small doses to which we are subjected. If atomic warfare does occur, a much larger portion of the human population may be menaced by large doses of radiation, and the whole flow of life from generation to generation may be seriously affected.

The very nature of life is a research goal. The living cell is the seat of life itself. An explanation of its protoplasm and the complex chemicals in many configurations which are contained within it may explain the nature of life. This is far more complex than any of the chemical processes of the ordinary factory or industry. The discovery of the structure of protein molecules may throw considerable light on the physical mechanism of life and living processes. A central problem in this truly vital matter is the structure of the genes within the chromosomes that are the bearers of heredity. Once we understand their composition and how they are modified by various means, we shall come closer to a solution. Only a minute portion of our research brains and resources are being spent on this fundamental problem.

We do not know the cause of life or even the ultimate facts about the mechanism of heredity. Nevertheless, so much has been learned about plant and animal breeding and hybridization that virtually new kinds of animals and plants have been created and will be created in the future. Science controls evolution in a very real sense. Hybrid corn, for instance, has added many millions of dollars to the agricultural resources of the world. Animal breeding, such as with cattle for better milk and beef production, aided by the widespread use of the technique of artificial insemination, has given astounding biological and economic results. Plants are bred to resist disease and withstand difficult environmental conditions. Even microorganisms are subjected to artificial evolution to make them into more deadly weapons for war, should that unhappy eventuality come. One-celled plants, algae, are selected and bred for their ability to capture the sun's energy most effectively.

The control of population is a future problem, although the time has not come and probably never will come when human population on the face of the earth can be planned and controlled in the same way that man regulates the hereditary future of animals and plants. But eugenics, which means better breeding biologically for the human race, has made some headway through the voluntary and enlightened understanding of the constant stream of parents of the future.

The introduction of modern medicine and sanitation in some of the already overpopulated portions of the world has released the biological brakes naturally present upon population growth. While the industrialization of an area seems to produce substitute limitations upon population, these have been slow to come into operation in many areas. There is, therefore, a gigantic race between food and people. Solutions developed by science and research are most difficult to apply to this population problem, but an intensive research approach might bring results.

Nature maintains a relatively even balance among the sexes, particularly among human beings. The approximate 50:50 ratio among males and females does not always exist in lower animals and plants. The control of human sex is not a probable development for the future, but a search is under way along various lines to influence the sex ratio in animals. The dairy industry would welcome a way of producing a predominant number of female calves that would grow up into good milk cows. Since the elements that control sex, the chromosomes, in the reproductive process are different for male and female, there is some chance of eventual success in this endeavor.

Despite many medical successes, there are vast unconquered areas in our world health picture. Most uncontrolled are the degenerative diseases, such as cancer, heart and circulatory disorders, nephritis, arthritis, diseases of the respiratory system, and ills of the brain. Least controlled of all the infectious diseases are those caused by the viruses, including colds. There is more chance of adequate support for medical research than for many other less "practical" objectives.

Many of the most important elements in the crust of the earth are in very limited supply. By means of geological processes, nature has concentrated some of these in ore deposits. Man has developed methods to extract these substances, such as the metals, iron, lead, tin, copper, etc., but has proceeded to dissipate them over the face of the earth by using them, discarding them, and thus losing them for posterity. For some of the prime metals we can synthesize replacements or substitute other natural elements more difficult to extract from their chemical combinations. Repeatedly, during the growth of our oil age, we have been told that the supply of petroleum will continue to be available for only a few years longer. From a long-time viewpoint this is true, although the discovery of more oil fields has kept pace with the prodigious increase in utilization. The same is true for natural gas. Of coal and oil shale we still have extensive deposits, which will however cost more to process into usable liquid fuel. But this can be done. To obtain many of the unrenewable materials essential to our present way of life, we must mine ore deposits of lessening richness or at greater distances from our industrial centers. Future generations must be satisfied with less ease in obtaining their essential elements, if they have not discovered some way by then to do without them.

There are some things on this globe that are essentially inexhaustible: the sunlight from which we should eventually be able to capture large-scale energy, the air with its oxygen and nitrogen, sea water rich in salts and already the mine of the metal magnesium, clay from which we have not been able to extract economically the aluminum that it contains, coal with its chemical storehouse of raw materials, sand with its tightly held silicon, etc. Some of these plebeian materials, almost as free as the air we breathe, may be found in future decades to be as valuable as the waste lands under which oil fields long existed undiscovered.

Synthetic chemistry, powered by atomic or photosynthetic energy, can reduce the difference between the have and have-not areas of the world. From almost any convenient source of carbon, hydrogen, and oxygen, a vast array of organic chemicals can be made, provided energy is also available. Coal, oil, oil shale, or even growing things can be the raw material for synthetic fibers, plastics, drugs, insecticides, and almost everything else industry and modern living demand. Assuming that the world will get over its military conflicts, its varied regions will be able to be more self-sufficient than they have been in the past, thanks to the scientific skill of synthesis. Amazingly interchangeable and fruitful as the application of chemistry has become, its potentialities for the future are even greater.

The high degree of mechanization of industrial processes foreshadows an almost automatic factory. Already a few men with the aid of many instruments and controls are able to operate large oil refineries night and day, for months on end. Mechanization, controlled by electronic devices and utilizing the intricacies of servomechanisms with tireless and precise skills unrivaled by human hand and eye, can take over many of the factory processes. We now need only energy and capital investment to create within our buildings artificial atmospheres neutralizing the winter's cold and the summer's heat through air conditioning. Life for most of us is unthinkable without an automobile, and even grass cutting is now mechanized. More and more, the human element comes into the mechanical world around us to keep the mechanism running rather than to provide the brawn or even the brains necessary in the pioneer frontier days.

The only real barriers to talking and seeing throughout the world will soon be those of political and ideological "curtains." We hear sounds in our living rooms which originate in literally all parts of the world that are free and accessible to us politically. Television will soon extend throughout the world. To travel by airplane to almost any part of the world, one needs only money and very little time. Any part of the world is only a day or two away from us.

Language is often a great barrier to prompt communication. The future promises to see this problem solved practically through the use of a satisfactory international language auxiliary to the existing natural languages. There have been many attempts to make an international language, but not until now has there been a careful and scientific study to produce one that can technically and emotionally serve this purpose. This linguistic invention, called *Interlingua,* is based on the Western languages. If it is given a chance, it should be able to solve this communications dilemma for science and technology, as well as for other fields of international interchange.

It is not too much to expect that, as and if the preoccupation with military defense yields to more peaceful living, we may have what amounts to a world brain which will give anyone access to the accumulated and stored knowledge of the world in all fields. Through mechanized devices that file and find information can be created a bookless library of the accumulated information of the world. What one wishes to know can be obtained by, in effect, pushing the proper button. Microfilm, and photographic enlargements from microfilm, will be one of the essential tools. Giant electronic calculators or "brains" will fit into the system, as will new and novel methods of classification based upon mathematical principles.

To discover the future and operate our increasingly scientific civilization, human talents and human abilities need to be discovered and cultivated. Psychological techniques have given us the means to discover human abilities. It is fortunate for the world that not everyone has the same abilities. There are those who excel in music, language, human relations, science technology, and other attributes.

Most important is the discovery and cherishing of scientific ability among our youth. Adequate teachers, inspired volunteers in the community and science clubs of our schools, science fairs, and the Science Talent Search are important in giving opportunity to youth who have ability and operating interest in science and technology.

To the extent that we understand ourselves and those with whom we live and work, we can build and promote the social peace necessary to an effective democracy. Techniques for aiding children to grow up into successful citizens have undergone extraordinary development. Their applications in coming years will bring more fundamental sanity into the future.

Mental ills, ranging from chronic grouches to disabling psychoses, do take major tolls in our civilization. Disordered and mentally warped personalities give rise to crimes of all sorts, including those against society. Included in the mystery of mind and emotions is the matter of human behavior, so important in the management, operation, and conduct of everything we do.

The control of the human factor in our civilization constitutes the greatest of the unsolved problems of science. It is the probable key to the prevention of war.

Implicit to all in the dissemination of science and its methods is the belief that if the people know the truth, it will not only keep them free, but allow them to act intelligently in the conduct of their social and personal lives. This may not be the whole story, if science is narrowly construed. But if the deep emotions, the hidden motivations, the biological and psychological remnants of our heredity and environment are knowable and controllable within the realm of science, then we can have some confidence that the impact of science upon humanity can mitigate the conflict and cruelty of man against man. We must believe that we can domesticate the human beast or breed out his bad genes.

Whatever is the outcome of this great and fateful chance for humanity through which we are living (and perhaps every generation has lived through a crisis as epochal to it), we have the obligation to do our best to keep aloft a full-blazing torch of science.

INDEX